PORTRAITS *of* SUCCESS

PORTRAITS *of* SUCCESS

Lupus Patients Who Celebrate Life

Text and Photography by
Barbara De Witt

With

Rodney Bluestone, M.B.

Christina Kelly

David Klashman, M.D.

Mary Weyand

Published by Lupus International
Irvine, California

Although the drugs and products mentioned in this book are used by many lupus patients, Lupus International does not necessarily endorse them.

Lupus International
17983 Sky Park Circle, Suite J
Irvine, California 92614

Published in collaboration with Angel City Press
2118 Wilshire Boulevard, #880
Santa Monica, California 90403
310-395-9982

First Published in 2006
Copyright © 2006 by Lupus International
ISBN-13/EAN: 978-0-9790601-0-6
ISBN-10: 0-9790601-0-9
Art direction and design: Amy Inouye, Future Studio
All photographs copyright © 2006 by Lupus International. Photos by Barbara De Witt except as noted here: Kathy Vara courtesy ABC7, Hayley Weinstein by Heather Hart of A La Mode Photo, Linda and Bobby Hatfield by Dave Cook Photography, Dolores Kroop by Jennifer Godwin-Minto, Barbara De Witt by Tina Burch of *Los Angeles Daily News*

Content Editor: Mary Weyand
Medical Editors: David Klashman, M.D. and Rodney Bluestone, M.B.
Text Editor: Susan Love Loughmiller

LIBRARY OF CONGRESS CATALOGING-IN-PUBLICATION DATA
Portraits of success : Lupus patients who celebrate life / by Barbara De Witt ... [et al.]. — 1st ed.
    p. cm.
ISBN 978-0-9790601-0-6 (trade pbk. : alk. paper)
1. Systemic lupus erythematosus—Patients—Biography. 2. Systemic lupus erythematosus—Patients—Portraits.
I. De Witt, Barbara.
RC924.5.L85L92 2006
362.196'7700922—dc22
                                    2006034404

Printed in U.S.A.

For the brave women and men who successfully find ways to live with lupus.
Their positive attitude will surely light the way for others.

*The predicted life span of a lupus patient is rapidly approaching
the predicted life span of someone without lupus.
There is literally an explosion of new knowledge and great new drugs on the horizon.
These medications will have greater efficacy and less toxicity.
They will be available in the not-too-distant future.*

—DAVID KLASHMAN, M.D.

CONTENTS

FOREWORD

Systemic Lupus Erythematosus (SLE), or lupus as it is called for short, is an autoimmune condition which causes inflammation in a variety of organs in the body, including the skin, kidneys, joints, lungs and heart. It affects individuals very differently. Some people have mild forms of the disease while other manifestations are life-threatening. Regardless of the severity, it clearly does affect people's lives.

Those who suffer from lupus are strong individuals from whom we can learn a great deal about life. One of them is Barbara De Witt, whom I have had the pleasure of taking care of for the past four years. Barbara has dealt courageously with her illness. With all of the ups and downs she has experienced, her cup has remained half full.

This positive attitude is very helpful when treating lupus, and she has worked hard to convey both the attitude and the message with this book.

While the cause of lupus remains unknown, we are starting to learn about genes that may contribute to the development of this condition. This knowledge will ultimately result in therapy that is better targeted toward lupus. In the meantime, there are numerous new and exciting drugs that are in development for the treatment of lupus.

Although there currently isn't a cure for this condition, I am optimistic about the future for our patients.

JENNIFER GROSSMAN, M.D.
Assistant Clinical Professor
David Geffen School of Medicine, UCLA

FOREWORD

When a patient with a chronic disease comes to the doctor, the key question is: What sort of disease do I have? The doctor has to address that question accurately, but must also give equal consideration to another question: What sort of patient has this disease?

It then becomes a question of the soil and the seed.

In this book, the seed is systemic lupus, with its numerous manifestations, with variable severities, complications and a constant backdrop of treatment side effects. And the soil is the patient.

What this book is really all about is the soil. The people profiled in the following pages will show you how they cope with their illness. They reveal their inner strengths and display the enormous importance of having a strong spirit, socioeconomic stability, education and knowledge, intact family and community support systems, and how these multi-faceted assets—the *quality* of the soil—largely govern the prognosis of their disease, no matter how potent the seed.

Lupus International is dedicated to the enrichment of the soil. We want to inform, guide, educate, reassure and support the patient dealing with systemic lupus. We know what it takes to cope with the challenge of systemic lupus and how crucial peer and physician guidance can be to ease the burden. Our volunteer scientists and physicians will ensure a dependable flow of medical advances and knowledge that we can disseminate to all concerned partners—the lupus patients and their health care providers. Our volunteer educators will disseminate an accurate base of knowledge and insight about the disease, its treatment and available community resources.

The board of directors of Lupus International will ensure a high visibility of the issues at hand and strive to raise funds for aiding enrichment of the patient *soil* and for specific therapy directed at the lupus *seed*.

Lupus International will continue to help patients and their families take control of the disease, and we will expand our efforts. The brave individuals profiled in this book will show you how it's done.

RODNEY BLUESTONE, M.B.
Chairman of the Board, Lupus International

PREFACE

My entire life has been in fashion's fast lane. I grew up in the world of beauty pageants, fashion shows and "makeovers," and my thirty-year career as a Fashion Editor was my dream job. I was busy traveling the world, winning awards, teaching fashion writing, schmoozing with celebs and even making TV appearances. Finally, I earned a mention in *Who's Who*. And then I got Systemic Lupus Erythematosus (SLE).

Life as I knew it came to a crashing halt on a summer night in 1999 when my husband rushed me to the emergency room because I was so swollen with edema I couldn't breathe (much less put on shoes). Sadly, it was not a food allergy, but an allergic reaction to my own body.

Looking back, those early symptoms weren't so bad. Over the past years this unglamorous disease with no cure has taken me on a major roller coaster ride with rashes, steroid-induced weight gains, hair loss, pneumonia, a thyroidectomy, bladder surgery, broken ribs, Raynaud's phenomenon, Cushing's syndrome, Calcinosis, cataracts, a bone marrow biopsy, tremors and fluid in the hips—forcing me to walk with a cane.

Suddenly, I was no longer fit for duty on Oscar's red carpet, the Beverly Hills society circuit or even working at my desk in the newsroom.

It took two years before I could come to terms with the disease I'd never heard of before my diagnosis. I felt sorry for myself; I lost friends and, eventually, my job.

Now, thanks to a team of great doctors, a supportive husband and an upbeat Lupus International support group, I've been able to find myself again.

And, you can too, with the help of this book.

So, toughen up. Set goals. Express your newfound empathy, force yourself to have a sense of humor and never lose faith.

BARBARA DE WITT
Los Angeles, 2006

ACKNOWLEDGMENTS

Many thanks to Lupus International for its educational interest and financial support of this book. And special thanks to Mary Weyand, secretary of the of the Lupus International Board of Directors and co-facilitator with me of the Conejo Valley Support Group.

Hugs to my rheumatologists, Dr. Jennifer Grossman of UCLA Medical Center and Dr. David Klashman of the Arthritis Treatment Center in Torrance, California, for not only sharing their expertise but providing unwavering emotional support of my project. Dr. Klashman once told me that just because I had lupus and could no longer work full-time, my life wasn't over. He said he'd be attending my book-signing party within ten years, and I'm holding him to it.

I also want to thank the lupus patients who allowed me to share their stories through photographs and words. They enlightened me, energized me and are clearly the true heroes of the book.

The members of the Conejo Valley Support Group also must be thanked for their many contributions—from survival tips to words of encouragement. And for just being there.

Another person who deserves recognition is my dear, patient husband Don De Witt. He often helped with the technical aspects of the book in its early stages and has been my constant cheerleader. He understood how much it meant to me to write a book unlike all the others out there—one that would give hope instead of fear to the newly-diagnosed lupus patient. And he never complained about my late nights at the computer and the many meetings the book required.

Publishers are routinely thanked, but Paddy Calistro of Angel City Press was more than a publisher. She was the guiding light from the very beginning, and made sure the project took flight.

EDITOR'S NOTE

The role of editor for *Portraits of Success* has been different than in the production of most books. In this case, the editor was privileged to join the author on numerous trips, each time to the homes or workplaces of those whose biographies appear in the book. The author brought along her handicapped placard, a cane, thumb splints, a sun shade, other sundry lupus-dictated accoutrements and a huge smile . . . always the smile.

Sometimes she'd stay in bed until just before I arrived because she was so sick. She was on chemo at the time. Her hair was falling out. Her hips hurt.

It didn't matter. Barbara was so darned excited to tell the story of those who dare to dream of better days that "little things" like today's "inconveniences" didn't matter.

She'd wear her signature red. Everything matched everything. She had perfect makeup, perky hairdo (although "thinner than it used to be," she assured me) and that smile. Off we'd go.

An amazing change came over her when we arrived. She pushed her pain to a corner of the room. She dallied with the light and makeup and hair. She coaxed smiles. She played with their kids or their dog. She found their passion for life and caught it in her camera lens.

To the great credit of each and every person and their families, they shared their story. Triumphs were trumpeted, pain recounted. Hopes were voiced, advice given thoughtfully.

Supporters of these wonderful people deserve a round of applause. A profound thanks to Paddy Calistro of Angel City Press for her many kindnesses. Thanks to Dr. David Klashman for the humor, hope and simplicity in his explanation of the many illnesses and conditions that lupus often entails. We appreciate Dr. Jennifer Grossman, who stole time from her busy schedule to provide a book foreword. Deepest appreciation to Dr. Rodney Bluestone for his abiding guidance and contributions. Christina Kelly, executive director of Lupus International, has devoted her time and attention to the pages of this book. Thanks to all of you.

To the well over one million people who have lupus, each life precious, each story unique, we applaud your courage and pray that we have represented you well.

MARY WEYAND
Secretary of the Board
Lupus International

INTRODUCTION

You may have thought you were crazy.

Maybe your friends and family did, too. Or, that you were just a whiner.

And perhaps doctors hadn't initially been able to explain your come-and-go rashes, fevers, allergies, aches and absolutely incredible fatigue.

At least now, you know the truth.

You aren't crazy. You have a real disease called lupus, but you can still have dreams. A life. And a future.

Lupus is not a death sentence, but it doesn't come with fanfare, either. Unfortunately, it is not one of the well-known diseases that get media attention. Despite near anonymity, lupus strikes more of us than the whole crowd of people who suffer from AIDS, leukemia, multiple sclerosis, cystic fibrosis and muscular dystrophy, according to researchers.

So you're not alone. To date, there are more than a million lupus patients in the United States. The number of Americans diagnosed with lupus has nearly tripled over the past four decades, according to a study by the Mayo Clinic, and that doesn't count the thousands more who have not yet been diagnosed. Lupus, which is *not* a communicable disease, is fast being recognized as a worldwide health problem, with more than fifty thousand lupus patients reported in the United Kingdom, and no readily available figures for South America, Africa and Asia.

Any dictionary will tell you *lupus* is the Latin word for wolf.

Yes, life with lupus is suddenly all about the big bad wolf.

Look up in the sky on a clear night and you might see Lupus, the constellation located within the Milky Way galaxy.

Look up at the big screen near Halloween time and you can see flicks such as *Wolfman* or *Dracula*, the vampire who sleeps by day and bites by night. Notice how lupus falls into the film noir genre of diseases? One can imagine that back in ancient times, a woman with a big red mark over her cheek who preferred to stay indoors until darkness, could have inspired a folk tale or two.

About that telltale rash. Some believe that the rash may have gotten its name because the classic lupus rash that extends over the bridge of the nose is similar to the markings on a wolf's face.

Regardless, the disease we know so well as lupus erythe-

Regardless, the disease we know so well as lupus erythematosus has been taking lives since the time of Hippocrates in ancient Greece. But it didn't get its official name until 1851 when a Frenchman named Pierre Cazenave figured the skin disorder needed an official Latin name for the medical community. It took a few more years before doctors realized that lupus wasn't just skin deep but actually could affect internal organs—and thus it became Systemic Lupus Erythematosus, or SLE.

Too bad nobody took the time to notice how the rash really looks a lot more like a butterfly gently fluttering over the face. The end result may be the same, but it's a lot prettier picture, as the butterfly is a symbol of hope and courage and new life.

Today, we're more informed about our health than ever before, and yet too many people know nothing about lupus—until they get it or a loved one dies of it.

Fortunately, today's medical community is able to deliver effective treatments that can not only prolong life but improve the *quality* of life.

Despite the many milestones in lupus research, lupus continues to be a disease that mystifies general practice doctors. Rheumatologists who specialize in lupus liken the disease to a roller coaster ride gone amok; sometimes, you're feeling just fine and then the coaster jerks around a corner and plunges you down into the valley of despair with flu-like symptoms, or worse. When Lucy told Charlie Brown in the beloved comic strip by Charles Schulz that she only wanted "ups," she well could have been talking about lupus.

Former First Lady Eleanor Roosevelt also could have been talking about lupus when she reportedly said, "You have to accept whatever comes, and the only important thing is that you meet it with the best you have to give."

Sounds simple, doesn't it?

The *best* you have to give.

That means more physicians willing to specialize in lupus.

More pharmaceutical firms searching for new treatments.

More funds for medical researchers finding a cure.

More lupus patients daring to dream of a better life.

They can because

they think they can.

—Virgil

CHAPTER 1

PORTRAITS *of* SUCCESS

ROBIN JESSEMAN

Keeping up with my busy kids, driving them to all their events and not letting them see me sick, which isn't easy. Once I couldn't even walk, and my daughter saw me crawling on the floor. She covered me up with blankets until my husband got home to help. My kids are older now and that helps a lot.

"I WAS SUFFOCATING.

"For some God-only-knows-why reason, I woke up to our house ablaze.

"The smoke hovered directly over me, my husband Jon and our three-month-old baby daughter.

"Jon ran down the stairs, choking and coughing, to get the garden hose to put out the fire. Realizing quickly that the fire was too out of control, he ran back to the stairs.

"They had collapsed.

"He climbed the wall and side structure of the staircase.

"I jumped two-and-a-half stories to the patio, hitting the balcony of the house on the way down.

"Jon dropped our baby to me.

"He jumped.

"Our baby girl suffered a head injury. Jon and I escaped relatively unscathed.

"Miraculously, we all healed.

"Our house burnt to the ground. Not one single thing was left.

"The firemen told me that most people don't wake up in that situation. I have no idea why I did. They also told me that had we lifted and carried the baby in the room she would have died, as her lungs were already filled with smoke.

"For some reason, Jon simply moved her laterally out the window.

"This incident in 1989 crystallized the importance of *life* for me. Anything, just anything that happened after that was not huge.

"My husband is now a fireman, an obvious decision after the fire for such a courageous man. His occupation does mean that I don't always have someone to share parental responsibilities, especially cooking. And although I call myself a domestic engineer, gourmet cooking and housekeeping are not a high priority."

She lives for her family, and tries to stay fit by running on her good days. At lupus support group meetings, Robin's wide grin, sparkling eyes and wild mane of hair make her stand out, and her laughter and generous helpings of hugs make her a vital part of the group.

Robin's always-upbeat attitude is probably due to her wonderful childhood. She, her parents and two sisters enjoyed a lavish brunch every Sunday. "My dad was a pharmacist and he would take us to the pharmacy, which was closed, after brunch. We had a couple of minutes to run through the pharmacy and pick things that we wanted. It was great fun. My dad and I had a special relationship, as I was so much like him. He took me on many trips with him. Once we went to Mexico and climbed the pyramids. We were then—and still are—great pals."

On a more sober note, Robin talks of the first symptoms of lupus. "I remember it clearly. I was seventeen, in college, and found myself falling asleep in my classes. Friends noticed I was slowing down and getting huge bruises on the inside of my legs. I eventually developed lupus, manifested by arthritis. My hair fell out, but so far I've had no organ involvement. And I also feel guilty that so many people gain weight on steroids and other drugs, but it has the opposite effect on me. Smells and tastes of food affect me, and I can't keep it down . . . so often I don't eat much."

If you have a child who has lupus, be sure they understand it isn't their fault, and quickly learn all you can about the disease and its effect. Try to make the bedroom comfortable with soft bedding, as skin is very sensitive at first. Room temperatures may need to be changed often, as drugs can wreak havoc with one's internal thermostat. Also know that those same drugs that are helping survival may affect and change the sense of taste. Favorite meals may now bring nausea. Above all, pour on love and affection. And remember, it's not your fault either.

When I first got sick, I lost weight, but with steroids I gained fifty pounds and lost my self-esteem. When you are a teenager, heavy and losing hair in chunks, the idea of dating is difficult. But, look, I'm stable now and my hair grew back thicker than ever!

SHEREE TRIES TO EXPLAIN HER HOPES and fears through journaling. Among the pages is her recollection of being twelve and walking with her cousin on a spring day, discovering a pitiful, mewing kitten in the bushes. He was bedraggled and underweight, seemingly lost and hungry. She struggled through the bushes and gently collected him into her cupped hands.

"He was pocket-sized then," she grins, holding her full-sized cat named Gizmo. "He is my one of my best friends and is always there for me."

Sheree claims many other best friends in close family members, including her mom, her brother and grandparents, all of whom share a home with Sheree. Then there's an aunt and uncle, myriad caring cousins and good friends who offer continuous support.

"I was only thirteen when I was diagnosed with SLE. I had the flu a lot, but it was after I'd gotten a hepatitis inoculation for school that my health suddenly changed. I had a lump on my arm like an allergic reaction, followed by swollen feet, the butterfly rash on my face, and muscle and joint pain. I ended up in the hospital with blood transfusions, followed by massive steroids and chemotherapy.

"Unbelievably, my fourth-fifth grade teacher, Miss Peters, showed up at Children's Hospital to see me a couple of years ago. In fact three other teachers visited me as well. I couldn't believe that those teachers would care that much about me.

Teachers have always inspired me, and their support makes me want to succeed.

"Even though my cousin died of lupus, I choose not to think about the possibility of dying. I have a lot of living to do. Plus I'm fortunate that there are more and better treatments today, than there were for my cousin."

Sheree's now eighteen, and for many her age, it's a magic number. For Sheree, it's a feeling of well being and a strong belief in her future.

"I've always loved art and want to be a graphic designer. I took Photoshop in my junior year and found that I'm good at it. I'm looking forward to graduating, with an eye toward continuing my education in graphic arts."

Don't give up, no matter what. Don't worry about mean things other kids might say and don't let the disease win. A support group will give you the strength to deal with the disease as well as the cruel moments. While I once felt like giving up at school, recently I have been on the honor roll and my goal is to go to college.

SHEREE SANTIAGO

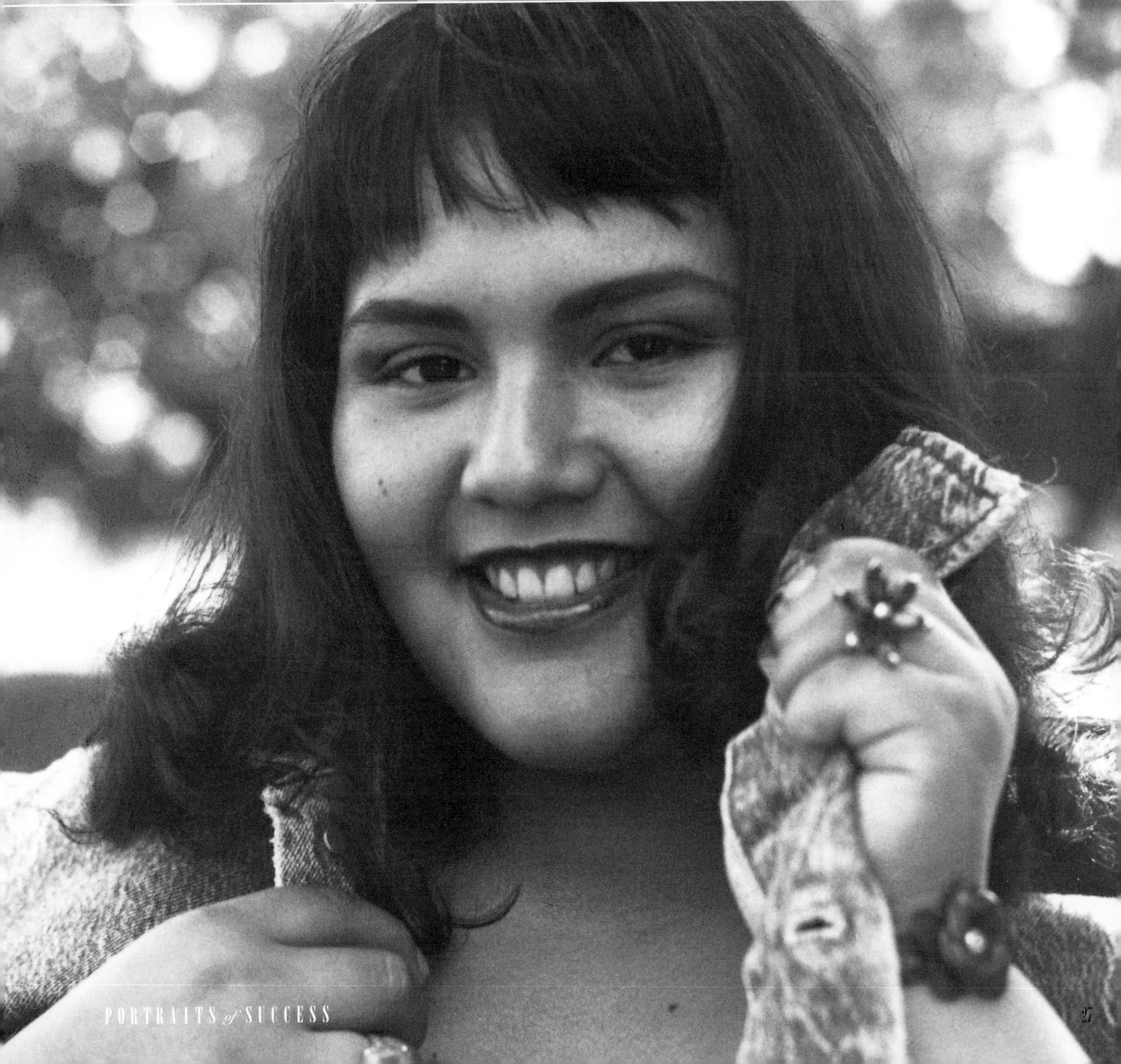

DOLORES KROOP

PORTRAITS *of* SUCCESS

My biggest challenge is fitting in all I want to do. There is never enough time or energy.
Learning to find a balance between being active and getting rest is difficult,
especially on the days when you wake up and feel almost normal, because you want to do it all.
That's when you have to really watch that you don't over do it.

"GROWING UP OVERSEAS I SAW MANY life altering diseases—leprosy, elephantiasis. I have always thought, 'How can I complain about what I am going through when there are people far worse off than me?' This has helped me realize that having lupus doesn't have to be the end of the world.

"My struggle began when my children, Gabrielle and Benjamin, came home with chicken pox. While caring for them I contracted chicken pox, too. But for an adult it is always more serious. In my case it was the beginning of lupus. It was hard to imagine a childhood disease could get an on-the-go mom down.

"It was three years before I was diagnosed with lupus, a thyroid condition called Hashimoto's disease and fibromyalgia. As strange as it may sound, I felt better once I was finally diagnosed. Just knowing that there was a name for what I was experiencing and that it was all real made it somehow okay. Don't get me wrong. Lupus is hard.

You have to deal with more than just the disease, but all that comes with it—side effects from medication, depression, lupus fog, and more.

"Lupus has affected my entire family. My children learned at an early age I was no longer Super Mom. I am not sure if that was harder on them or me. I've learned that I can be a super mom without trying to be Super Mom. We have all learned that simple things are now bigger deals. Everything has become a readjustment.

"Just as I began to cope with my disease, my daughter was diagnosed with lupus while a freshman at Loyola University. Now, she is almost finished with school. Sure, she's had to take time off, but Gabrielle has never given up."

Lupus hasn't stopped Dolores. It doesn't define who she is. She is a wife, mother, renowned interior/exterior designer, family business-owner of Padua Designs Showroom and philanthropist. Yes, it has

changed the way in which she lives, but lupus has not put a halt to her activities. She still participates in the Pasadena Showcase House of Design, West Coast Style Show, HGTV and many more.

Always willing to help others, she has raised millions of dollars over the last twenty years for a number of causes. Admittedly, she now has to make choices—choices not just related to living with this disease, but about taking on new clients, doing philanthropic work or scheduling social activities.

Dolores finds when she pushes too hard, there are repercussions—sometimes that means staying in bed for a few days.

"You train yourself to know how much is too much. That is my greatest challenge. How do you say 'no' to something you love doing? It is the essence of learning that you can have a rich life, by focusing on what you can do, rather than what you can't."

Redefine normal. You don't have to give up everything you enjoy. You just have to adjust to
how and when you can do it. And savor it. I loved to needlepoint all day. Now I can't.
So I work on it during time slots, use a magnifying glass and special lights.
This way I don't over stress my eyes or joints. Most importantly, don't ever give up.

I must admit that it seems like the focus of my daily activity is doctors' appointments, prescription medicines and the resulting side effects. We struggle financially because of the cost of required medical attention and drugs. I have been angry about being in this situation.

"I GREW UP IN ROSEMERE, A LITTLE town twenty-five miles north of Montreal, in the province of Quebec, Canada. It is a celebrated village, frequently referred to as the Hamptons of Montreal. The town was named for its population of wild roses. I can honestly say that I felt like a wild rose myself. I arrived unexpectedly, eight years after my nearest sibling. As an 'oops baby,' I had to fend for myself. My parents seemed to be done with parenting.

"My Aunt Doris was my saving grace. She and my uncle's household gave me some semblance of normalcy. They lived around the corner from our house and their home was my home. I was *always* there. I felt welcome and an integral part of their family. During my grade school years, my sisters

were grown up and on their own. Both of my parents worked, and I was raised like an only child. Luckily, I had twenty-one first cousins, many great-aunts, aunts and uncles, and Poppa, my mother's father. I am forever grateful for my extended family.

"As a teenager, I was totally enthralled with *Seventeen* and other magazines that featured fashion models. Being tall, blonde and pretty (at least that was what I was told), I thought I might have a chance at modeling. I took modeling courses from the top modeling agency in Montreal.

"The need for a steady income emerged, as occasional modeling assignments didn't support me. I landed a good job as a laboratory technician in the equine industry. I excelled at my work. During this

same time period, I met my husband Dave, fell in love and got married. After seven years, my consistently good health began to slip away.

"My symptoms started when I was about thirty, with extremely severe leg cramps that remained undiagnosed. From there, breathing difficulties occurred, which would be diagnosed as asthma. It was determined by a lung tissue biopsy (broncoscopy) at the UC San Diego Medical Center that it was due to chemical exposure from my career, and I was prescribed inhaled steroids that eventually led to the onset of adrenal insufficiency disease. Six months later, I had lupus."

Now I'm getting it. I have learned how I can make a difference in this world. I know, on a new level of understanding, that people need kindness. My goal in life is to be unconditionally loving, considerate and compassionate toward everyone I meet. I am really working on that, in my daily life.

JANICE E. REICH

FRANCINE BRISCOE

Dealing with the fatigue while keeping my job has been difficult. There are days when I've been too tired to go on patrol, which requires driving, but the LAPD (Los Angeles Police Department) has really understood and has allowed me to be on daytime patrol. And, on really bad days, I'm able to work on a computer at home. Then, there's my hands. I now have metal plates and screws in them and have lost dexterity, so I've had to learn new ways to do ordinary things such as buttoning clothing, writing and opening doors. But I still haven't figured out how to scratch my back!

"I WAS FIRST DIAGNOSED WITH LUPUS in 1994, right after my thirtieth birthday. I was working the graveyard shift and driving a patrol car and started feeling terribly tired even though I'd sleep for fifteen to sixteen hours before clocking in. I was achy, then got a rash from the sun. So after a series of tests, they gave me the news: I had SLE.

"I remember calling my father right away because he had lupus . . . and he died that same year, after it affected his heart. Losing him was very sad. Before his passing, I continued to run as much as I wanted—in the sun, too! I won lots of awards for my running achievements—many of which were first-place gold medals. I continued to pursue my workouts and work with greater vigor. I was determined to not let lupus win. Which meant I was not going to change my routine and I would continue to do what I wanted. I really thought if I pushed myself enough, I could still have it all. Then I started losing my long hair. When I had to cut it . . . well, that is a whole other story.

"Now here I was, diagnosed with this disease that just killed my dad. I was scared. Apparently that was what I needed, so that I would finally start taking care of myself. You can choose to ignore your symptoms, but they will find you eventually. You can't run from lupus, no matter how hard you try. I now give myself permission to miss workouts—that was unheard of before.

"Over the years, I've tried numerous medications from steroids and methotrexate to Imuran and Plaquenil as the disease progressed to arthritic pain, reconstructive hand surgeries and finally pernicious anemia, which now requires iron infusions instead of pills."

Be willing to alter your lifestyle. Don't dwell on the negative. And don't beat yourself up about things. I used to be an avid runner; now I'm happy to just run on a treadmill at home. I encourage new lupus patients to find a doctor who is familiar with lupus and will help you manage the side effects of medications needed to control the disease. Mostly, I regret not being able to have a child, but I'm so lucky to be surrounded with beautiful nieces and nephews who love me. I surely love them.

Most of the time I feel great. Sometimes I try to do too much and then I get a little reminder. My career is on track and I have even found the energy to enjoy a hobby that has become a passion for me: horseback riding. Ten years ago there were days I couldn't get out of bed and now I take riding lessons each week and am slowly improving. I'd even love to compete in a show someday!

FOR YEARS WE'VE SEEN KATHY VARA'S smiling face and heard her soothing voice deliver the morning news. You'd never guess she suffers from lupus, but the co-anchor of ABC7 *Eyewitness News* in Los Angeles has managed to have a fulfilling life by being upfront with her employers about her health needs and accepting the support of her husband and parents.

For all of her efforts Kathy has been nominated for two Emmy awards and received two Golden Mike awards for Best Daytime Newscast. Kathy also has received a Women of Courage Award from the City of Los Angeles and the national Hispanic Heritage Award from former President Bill Clinton. She is an honorary member of Lupus International's board of directors.

"I was diagnosed with SLE in 1994. It was terrible timing. I had just accepted a job to anchor morning news in Los Angeles. This was a big move for me. Of course I had no idea of the challenge I was really about to face. At first I tried to keep up with twelve-hour days that were part of the job, but I felt worse and worse. It wasn't until I was visiting my family in Texas that I had a total meltdown and could no longer mask my symptoms. My mother, a registered nurse, saw my swollen feet and rushed me to the hospital. My blood levels were so sky-high that the lab ran them three times in disbelief.

"I have to say I have been very lucky. I have loving parents and a wonderful husband. My mother moved in with us for several months to help. I did manage to keep my job, but worked far fewer hours. For the first year I rarely left the house except to go to work.

"Now I have learned to deal with the many strange and varied symptoms of lupus. I even feel comfortable telling the people at work, "I am not well today . . . it's a lupus thing . . . give me a day and I'll be better." If not I might be out for a month! I have been blessed with an extraordinary boss at ABC7, general manager Arnie Kleiner. He and vice president\news director Cheryl Fair have gone above and beyond to allow me to have a career along with a fulfilling life.

"Then there is former KNBC general manager Carol Black, who stood by me when I didn't know if I'd ever work again. Her exact words to me after I was diagnosed were, "Don't worry about a thing. I had a friend with lupus who didn't take care of herself and died when she was only thirty-six. I am not going to let that happen to you."

Look at the bright side. You now know why you feel awful and guess what? There is medicine that can help you feel better. Make sure you find a good doctor, someone who is experienced in treating lupus and is a good listener. Communication between a doctor and patient is key to successful living with this disease. And if possible, have a good relationship with your pharmacist, who can help you sort through any insurance problems. Lupus International is an example of an excellent organization that can help with information and support. Don't get discouraged. And always tell friends when you need rest. They will understand.

KATHY VARA

MARY ELIZABETH McDONOUGH

Lupus changes your life. Your day-to-day is different. I wasn't able to do all the physical things I did before, like walking up stairs or playing with my daughter. It can be emotionally debilitating, as well. Chronic illness can bring feelings of loss, weakness, fear and uselessness. But when you get proper care and information, you can manage your self-care. Then feelings of accomplishments replace the emotions. I'm better now, and so far in 2005, I ran my first 5K and have jumped tandem out of an airplane. My family calls me a daredevil. I think I am living.

"IT WAS IMMENSE PRESSURE.

"I didn't feel that I was good enough."

So said Mary McDonough, a celebrated actress, producer, director, writer and also a mother who is best known for her childhood role as Erin in the long-running television drama *The Waltons*.

"I was only ten when I was picked for the show. I was shy and nervous, very unsure of myself, even into my teens. It was not a normal way to grow up."

Mary took steps, as a fifteen-year-old, to address her feelings of dread. "I took scuba diving lessons and became an internationally certified scuba diver. I began to conquer things that scared me, and, as a result, my self-confidence began to grow.

A year later, her father died of colon cancer.

"It broke my heart, as he was—and is—my hero. He was a Nebraska farmer, a man who loved life. When we moved to California, he would spontaneously pile us four kids in the car and look for a new experience. One day it was horseback riding, another it was joyriding down sand dunes on our bottoms. His big spirit molded mine. My daughter Sydnee's middle name is Lawrence in honor of my father. I really miss him.

"I wanted more sophisticated roles as I matured. I thought breast implants might help my image. Instead, they almost killed me by triggering lupus. Once they were removed, I became healthier, although I still have lupus. I have taken a public stand on the dangers of implants and the cost of vanity. I do everything I can to bring attention to lupus awareness. I even played a lupus patient in the TV series *ER*.

"I know people don't always believe the link, but I believe my ruptured silicone implants triggered my immune responses and lupus. But now, with care and awareness, I am much better. And sun-screening everything (to avoid a potential flare) is one way my life changed."

"Always give something back, Mary," my father said to me on many occasions. "You're very lucky," he'd say.

"Standing beside the Capitol building in Washington, D.C., as I prepared to lobby Congress for women's health issues, I thought my father would never have dreamed of being here. I know he'd be very proud of me. He taught me activism. I am usually working for at least three charities at once. I'm giving back."

Challenge yourself. Set goals for yourself mentally, physically and emotionally. Make a positive choice to learn about the how, what and why of your illness, but don't get caught up in bad news or "what if"s. Expect the good. Open yourself to healing.

I was diagnosed when my two sons were small. My appearance changed so much—I got moon-faced and achy—and I think lupus affected my marital relationship and had a role in our divorce. It also made it hard to work at my career and still be "Super Mom."

"ALOHA."

"I was born on the island of Kauai, the oldest of the Hawaiian Islands. My childhood was full of fun, laughter and activities. Grandma and Grandpa Nakamoto, my mother's parents, lived at Paia, Maui, on the beach cliff. My brothers and I would spend summers with them, climbing down the rocks to the ocean everyday. We would pick seaweed for grandma to cook. We would bathe in an outdoor wooden tub and grandma would make us 'fat pancakes.' It was idyllic, a glorious childhood.

"In his elder years, my grandpa and I conversed on many topics. We exchanged books and poems. He did small watercolor paintings of birds and plants, or drew cartoons when he wrote cards and letters. When Grandpa went to meet Grandma in the afterlife, a part of us went with him. And a part of him stayed with us. My grandparents and my parents were marvelous, loving, creative people who inspired my whole life."

Today, Joanne oozes love and laughter from every pore. She uses the lessons of childhood in her work as a registered nurse, toting her banjo to a patient's side when they need to sing the blues away. She can be found singing with Village Voices Chorale or donating time to the Diabetes Bicycle Tour or the Love Run for Meals on Wheels with her hospital team, at an age when others are thinking about retirement.

Joanne's exuberance has helped her survive troubling times.

"I was twenty-eight, raising my two small children, and my hair started falling out in patches and I was fatigued. When I discovered a small lesion on my cheek and thought I had acne, I went to a dermatologist. Well, I didn't have acne. After seeing numerous specialists, I finally was diagnosed with lupus by a rheumatologist who also explained that the disease had affected my kidney. For more than twenty years I took steroids and other drugs, but then I seemed to grow out of the illness and tapered off the steroids. Today, I am in total remission. So, just be patient, it could happen to you."

If you are married, your spouse may feel left out when everybody is worrying about you and bringing you gifts and flowers and you are wrapped up with lupus. To protect your marriage, talk about your new condition with him or her early in the diagnosis and make time to do the things you did before, such as going out to breakfast, the movies and romance. In other words, don't let your spouse feel sidelined. I also like to think that if you can accept your difficulties, you can crush them in your embrace.

JOANNE CHANG

Occupati
Therapy

JOANNE
RN, COHN

Well, I have always been a real go-getter and was working my way up the career ladder. Then I had to stop working. That was tough for me. One of the biggest challenges for me is to give myself credit for what I have accomplished instead of beating myself up for what I am unable to do. I struggle with this daily.

"IT WAS THE MOST AMAZING MOMENT of my life. My adopted son, Jason, was born June 2, 2005 at 5:53 A.M. He weighed eight pounds, ten ounces. Jason's birthmother wanted us to be as much a part of his birth as if I had carried him myself, so my husband, Evan, cut the umbilical cord and I was the first to hold him. I felt an immediate bond and, when I arrived home with Jason in my arms, I felt a sense of calm and happiness that I have never felt before. After struggling to find purpose while living with lupus, I now feel like I know what I am supposed to be doing for the first time in my life. I know it will be challenging, but I know it will be worth it because we worked so hard to create our family," Hayley said with a huge smile. "After two years of fertility shots, failed adoption matches and hormonal hell, we finally have the family we have dreamed of for years.

"I met my husband, Evan, when a mutual friend set us up on a blind date. I remember not feeling well the day of the date (a precursor to my diagnosis) and considered canceling the date. Somehow, out of courtesy, I mustered the energy to get dressed and head out for the date. After only five minutes of talking with Evan I realized I was on the best date of my life. He made me laugh, had great stories, had talent and drive, and was a perfect gentleman. Six months later he asked me to marry him, and I said, 'YES!'

"I was diagnosed in January of 1999, but the symptoms started nine months earlier, on the first day of our honeymoon as we strolled the French Quarter in New Orleans. I was halted by a sudden wave of fatigue and I felt faint. Doctors assumed it was brought on by a thyroid condition I'd had since the age of twelve, but the pain and fatigue increased, and I began to have trouble concentrating. More than once I fell asleep at my desk—I also noticed memory problems, and really feared I'd be fired from my job. Then, I got so sick I had to be hospitalized, and I was finally diagnosed with lupus-associated hemolytic anemia.

"I told my husband it would be okay if he wanted to leave me, since he hadn't signed up for a chronically ill wife, but Evan has been supportive of me throughout my illness. His primary concern is for my health and well-being. He has put up with my wacky mood swings, my chronic pain, my depression and my hospital visits at the most inopportune times. He even had a second honeymoon planned for our fifth anniversary, but I tripped three days before we were to leave and shattered my kneecap. He spent his entire vacation taking care of his klutzy, accident-prone wife—but never a complaint from him. No wonder he's a four-time Emmy winner as co-executive producer of CBS's *The Amazing Race.* He's an amazingly supportive, loving husband."

If you have memory problems, invest in a personal digital assistant (PDA), like a Blackberry or Palm Pilot, to keep your life in order, or at least keep must-do lists. And keep a journal because details can become a blur. Also, accept that mourning the loss of your old self is okay. But still keep up your appearance—get out of pajamas, fix your hair, put on makeup and dress up. If all else fails, let a therapist help you.

I put myself through college to have a career I loved. Being a therapist was my life . . . how I defined myself. And now I have to work through my identity crisis, which is more challenging than I'd ever expected. I never know what to say when someone asks what I do, but a friend told me that I'm still a counselor. I also have to deal with guilt about using my handicapped placard since I don't always look sick. Also, I accept having bad days when I don't feel well enough to meet friends for social events.

OUTSPOKEN.

Fiercely loyal.

Puts family first. Hers and any family in trouble.

That's how friends and co-workers define her exterior, and inside she's got tenacious courage. When she sees a problem, she wants to fix it - whether it's a teen at risk or her own disease.

She is way past the "Why me?" level when it comes to lupus. Now in her forties, she recalls how she went from doctor to doctor, complaining of excruciating headaches, low fevers and flu-like symptoms.

"Of course, I became depressed," says Karen, who is clearly an achiever, who has no time for headaches and down days. Finally, she got a doctor who said he'd stay with her until they found out what was really wrong, she recalls. It was a bittersweet victory, as the diagnosis was Lupus Cerebritis, a controversial form of SLE. It was diagnosed by a lumbar puncture and an MRI of the brain, which showed mini-strokes and vasculitis.

"At least I could finally put a name on my angst," she says, adding that although she is now on numerous medications, the disease is still active with newfound complications such as Hashimoto's disease that affects the thyroid, pernicious anemia and pericarditis. She's currently undergoing numerous rounds of oral surgery as well, so she's no longer able to work at the job that not only gave her a salary, but the self-esteem that comes from achieving one's goals.

She's talking about her career as a psychotherapist who specialized in emotionally disturbed and abused adolescents.

Now she deals with her own battles and fights back by pushing herself to the limit with the ancient French philosophy of Pilates, which helps build inner strength. Then there are voice lessons. For many lupus patients, thyroid problems cause hoarseness and even complete loss of vocal cord use— but Karen is now able to sing at local charity events.

At home, she is wife to a high school educator and mom to the family dog, Sparkie. From Karen's earliest memory, she says she always knew her six siblings and large extended family were there for her.

"When trouble came, there was always support and help, but I saw that other children were not so lucky. I think that becoming a psychotherapist was a way to right the things that were wrong for them," she explains.

For twenty-five years Karen worked with literally hundreds of children, some at schools for the emotionally disturbed, others in foster homes—and also gang members.

"As a counselor, you know you can't help everyone, but every success story can validate you for life. Lupus has taken away my ability to work right now, but a new passion and reason for my experience in the field of psychotherapy is just around the corner."

If lupus has forced you to quit your job, try volunteer work if you are able. It's especially helpful when you're not ready to retire. Try Pilates to keep your muscles strong, and talk to your doctor about patches for nerve and muscle pain, and don't feel guilty about loving chocolate. When you get well enough to discontinue your steroids, you'll have a new outlook on life. And maybe you won't need the chocolate anymore. Finally, learn to be grateful for small pleasures. For instance, be happy for one slow dance with your lover instead of being upset that you no longer can dance all night.

KAREN STAVE

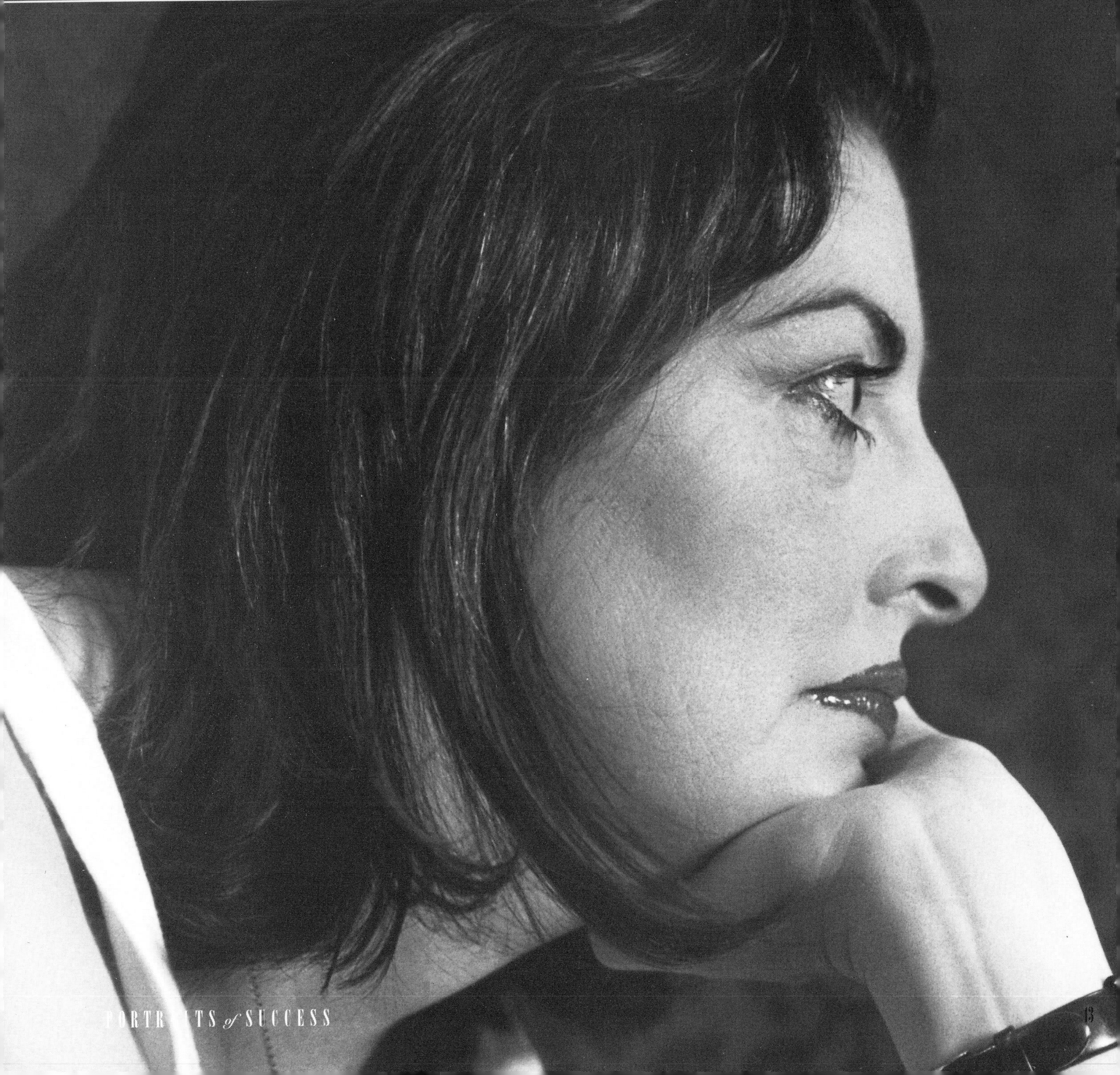

LAUREN SHULER DONNER

The most trouble I have dealing with lupus is my energy level. It is exhausting just to think; I can't speak by the end of the day. I have sat in my car in the garage at the end of the day because I am too weak and exhausted to get out. Fortunately, I have a wonderful, supportive and understanding husband. I have been able to be prolific in my career but only because I used prednisone to supplant my energy level. Sometimes, when I am overcome with a problem, I can't shut out of my brain, so I put a bubble around the problem and watch it float away until it is so tiny, it disappears.

LAUREN HAS PRODUCED NEARLY TWO dozen feature films that have generated billions of dollars in revenue and earned Oscar nominations and scores of awards. Among her films are *St. Elmo's Fire, Pretty in Pink, You've Got Mail* and *Constantine.*

You can picture her incredibly fast-paced life by looking at her most recent accomplishments: *She's the Man,* a teen comedy based on Shakespeare's *Twelfth Night; X-Men: The Last Stand,* the third in this series; *Unaccompanied Minors,* a comedy in the vein of *The Breakfast Club* meets *Home Alone* and the 2006 release, *The Secret Life of Bees,* based on the popular book.

Lauren has a strong personal drive to achieve, and she works through her pain and fatigue with exercise, a low-carb diet and medications as needed. Her doctor is trying a new one to keep her functioning. Medicines work, and then they don't, and then you try to find a new one. Lauren is a Hollywood genius and celebrity, but the disease cares not.

Like many lupus sufferers, Lauren was misdiagnosed for many years. "I probably had lupus in my mid-to-late twenties long before anyone figured out what it was. My doctor insisted over and over again it was kidney problems, since I was plagued with kidney infections and stones as a child. I was thirty-three when I was finally diagnosed. I think my mother also had lupus, since she always had a mysterious illness with symptoms similar to mine. Unfortunately, she died when she was fifty-four—before I was diagnosed."

Lauren has her list—her list of lupus symptoms—and can rattle them off, as so many of us can. "I am affected by lupus with extreme fatigue, low-grade fevers, anemia and neck and shoulder pain that sometimes creates a paralysis. My brain doesn't function well; I feel like I am in a fog at times; I have Raynaud's phenomenon that affects my fingers and lupus-related fibromyalgia." It's not a pretty list.

But she succeeds in the tough business of Hollywood, and somehow she makes time for others. In addition to her film career, she served on the board of Hollygrove Children and Family Services. "A friend introduced me to Hollygrove, and I was very impressed with the caring staff and the facility." Hollygrove is a child-centered, family-focused community organization serving abused and neglected children and those at risk of abuse.

Lauren has served on advisory boards for a number of organizations including: the Science Fiction Museum and Hall of Fame in Seattle; Producers Guild of America; Academy of Motion Picture Arts and Sciences, Producer's Branch, Planned Parenthood, and Natural Resources Defense Council. Lauren has been honored by Girls, Inc., for inspiring young girls to be all they can be—with or without lupus.

She and husband Richard Donner were honored by Mikhail Gorbachev's environmental organization, Global Green USA, with its 2000 Green Cross Millennium Award for Entertainment Industry Environmental Leadership for their tireless efforts to protect the Earth for future generations. In July 2006, Lauren and Richard received the American Cancer Spirit XXII Award.

My advice to the newly-diagnosed is to understand that this disease is not the end of the world. Despite being ill (or maybe because of it?), I have been able to produce twenty-two movies and have a wonderful marriage. Positive thinking, a good sense of humor, slow deep-breathing, music and meditation are key. Rest is essential; it is both the cure—if you have enough of it— and the cause—if you don't.

I have antiphospholipid antibody syndrome, and it is often frustrating to try to explain my health problems to doctors who are unfamiliar with this syndrome that conventional medical practices don't work for me. It also delays medical procedures such as biopsies and surgery.

KEEP YOUR LIFE—NOT LUPUS—IN the forefront.

"I don't know if it's the key to success for everyone, but it works for me," says Tim, a thirty-nine-year-old news systems editor for the *Los Angeles Daily News* and its sister papers in the Los Angeles Newspaper Group. A problem solver by nature, he tackles computer problems at work, and then looks for ways to solve his own.

"I have lupus, but to stay healthy, I put my job, family, home and hobbies, such as roller-blading or going to the theater, first. I also like hanging out with friends, but I try to minimize my health problems as much as possible in our conversations and don't dwell on how many medicines I take a day."

When it comes to his career and his doctor appointments, Tim calls it a real juggling act. He often works six-day weeks and still manages to see his rheumatologist, hematologist, eye doctor and others who monitor his medications and keep him stable. He primarily relies on Western medicine that includes the antimalarial drug Plaquenil but also has tried several Eastern medical practices to relieve the stress that can cause a

flare. Among them are acupuncture, meditation and a form of slow movement called quqong. He stresses that his health plan is not unique—that more and more lupus doctors and patients are recognizing the benefits of multicultural health regimens.

But he thinks his change of diet has made the biggest difference.

"Several years ago, before I'd been diagnosed with lupus, I happened to watch a TV program about patients whose health benefited by eliminating meat from their diets. I thought it sounded like a good idea since I already had blood clotting problems and now I'm a strict lacto-ova vegetarian, which means I eat milk, eggs, cheese and other dairy products as well as vegetables and fruits. The diet change didn't stop the blood clots, but I like to think it has slowed down my condition."

Although Tim recalls having lupus symptoms since high school, he wasn't diagnosed until he was thirty-one. Like other lupus patients, Tim has suffered from a red rash on his cheeks and several lupus-related problems, but he remains relatively stable and recently took his first trip abroad where

he found London the city in which he'd like to live at some time in the future—when he's ready to live at a slower pace.

A quiet, even-tempered man, lupus has taught him real compassion. He always has a hug and word of encouragement for others in his lupus support group, and the kindness he shares comes back to him full circle.

"My attitude probably stems from my family life. I'm the youngest of five children and grew up at the foot of Mount Timpanogas along the Wasatch Mountains of Utah. Then and now I have had a good, solid family support system and always felt loved. My upbringing gave me the inner strength to deal with lupus and not feel devastated or out of control."

That inner strength Tim refers to gave him the courage to leave the safety of a small book-publishing firm that treated him like family and try his skills at a major newspaper chain. "That step changed my life and career path, but it's a career I enjoy enough to get me through the rough spots of my illness."

Be happy. It takes mental discipline, but it makes living with lupus easier. See your doctor regularly. Take and monitor your medications but don't be afraid to question your doctors about alternative solutions, such as acupuncture, which I found is good for depression as well as pain. Or trading beef for tofu.

ANGELA MONTEILH

Learning to be the new person you have become, whether it's loss of hair or steroid-induced weight. It's also trying to still feel useful and have an active part in society. Each person has to find her way, but for me, it's volunteering a few hours on my good days at my family's day care center. It not only has helped me feel less depressed but keeps me in touch with the outside world.

ANGELA GREW UP IN SOUTHERN California, graduating from Pacific Palisades High School. After earning her degree from California State University, Long Beach, she worked as an electrical engineer and married her soul mate and life partner, Christopher Monteilh.

"At thirty-two I delivered a still-born child. Then I started having panic attacks, but doctors said it was just post-partum blues. I knew it wasn't. I got pleurisy. My fingers stopped working and my knees swelled up. It affected my vocal chords, making me lose my voice for weeks at a time. Then I lost my hair and became so sick that—like others with lupus—I had to leave my job."

Recalling those early days, Angela says she felt very scared and alone, but her husband told her he was the there for her and has continually given her the courage to fight the disease and its symptoms.

Now forty-five, Angela has survived the worst and has three beautiful, dynamic children whom she describes as the joy of her life.

"I have a wonderful husband who is my best friend, an amazing twin sister and two older sisters whom I can always count on. We were raised by our mother who worked hard every day of her life, so she could provide for her children. I now realize how difficult it must have been for her but she never let us know the sacrifices she must have made. I remain in awe of my mother," says Angela, who adds that her mother's example has served as a blueprint for her own parenting experience.

Life has certainly not been the way she planned or dreamed. Yet Angela has adapted with grace. She creates an attractive appearance even when she has to walk with a cane. She doesn't let her children know every detail of her illness and even tries to water-ski with them. But, since she is sun-sensitive and tires easily, she plans her activities early in the morning or at dusk.

At the end of the day I would not change a thing. I've learned to like my new life. But I advise parents to talk to your children about your illness, sparing some of the details. Don't allow them to be with you during your medical procedures. Talk about a family partnership of helping each other and learning to pull one's weight. For instance, my youngest son can cook! I believe this philosophy makes children better people and gives them the opportunity to rise to the occasion. Finally, assure your children that although you are sick, you are going to get well with their help.

Smart and analytical, Rebecca has the unique ability to step outside of herself and see the challenge for what it is. "The disease is frustrating . . . it's always something. Right now, I'd like to be able to eat and keep food down. I'd like to be able to take a shower without needing my mom nearby. I'd like to go to school and have a normal life. But I'm against being depressed about it."

"MOM, I MADE VARSITY! CAN YOU believe it?" Rebecca yelled as she bounced in the door from school a few years ago.

Rebecca knew her mom would be home. She always was.

And, Rebecca knew that her Mom would be the first one to applaud another success in Rebecca's life, as her young daughter, a sophomore, announced a coveted spot on the high school varsity women's basketball team.

"My mom is my hero. She mustered up the courage to leave a bad marriage and strike out on her own. Not easy for a woman with four children. She started an in-home business, so she could continue to be available to her children. Can you imagine? The business is QuakeKare. We supply emergency preparedness supplies, and even supply the Red Cross. She is incredibly successful and I love her to pieces,"

Becca's fondest memories are of horse-playing with her three older brothers when she was a kid. "They didn't seem to get that I was a *girl* and different from them," she says with a grin. "We each sent a sibling to the hospital for stitches or something like that as we were growing up. So I guess I must've gotten even with them at some point."

At twenty-one years young, Rebecca still loves sports. "I'm a good swimmer and was on the grade school and junior high school swim teams. I'd really like to get back to that," she daydreams. "Right now, I'm wrestling with lupus."

"When I was about fifteen, I was diagnosed with autoimmune disease, but it took another year before I was actually diagnosed with SLE. That's systemic lupus, and it has hit most of my systems, beginning with my kidneys, heart, lungs and then my brain, muscles and, of course, my joints. I've endured numerous surgeries, and right now I'm recovering from a colon biopsy.

When I was in high school, people thought I was an abused child because I was always bruised or wearing a cast or bandage. Finally, later on in my sophomore year, I quit going to school. I studied at home and teachers brought the tests to me and I graduated. Now I enroll for college every semester and try to attend as much as possible. Because of all my "experience" with the medical field, I want to work in bio-medical engineering. Continuing my education is very important to me."

Rebecca reflects, "Once more I can say that my mom is a total hero. She and my stepdad have been there for me every step of this difficult journey. This much happening to your only daughter is certainly tough on them."

Newly diagnosed teens need to be realistic and also optimistic. Sickness and injuries will take longer to heal, and if you don't take care of yourself you won't be able to do anything.

Also, find a doctor who doesn't ignore you and takes the time to explain things, returns your calls and doesn't tell you to just go to an emergency room because he's busy. And don't be embarrassed about getting a second or third opinion for surgery. In other words, don't just settle.

Also, when you are sick and bedridden, think about what you're going to do in the future. I have dreams of a home, family and a career.

REBECCA BARTHOLOMEW

I still ache and need to pace myself and remember to rest. I don't have time for lupus!
But boy, does it remind me it's still there. Listen to your body and take care of yourself.
No one else will.

"I WAS DIAGNOSED WITH LUPUS IN 1988, about the same time my husband's cousin died from lupus. It was frightening to my family and me. I wasn't ready to die. My husband Dickson and I planned a life together; our children Brandon and Tamara were small; and I had a flourishing career. To me, family is everything, and I couldn't imagine not being here for them.

"Initially my symptoms ranged from hair loss to kidney failure and everything in between. Back then doctors didn't know as much about lupus and weren't able to offer the same type of support they can today. At first they thought I might have tuberculosis, Lyme disease or malaria. I didn't. It was definitely lupus nephritis and Sjogren's Syndrome. Because my kidney function was so low, I was placed on very high doses of Prednisone. And once my kidneys started working again, instead of tapering me off, they abruptly stopped the steroids. That turned out to be a mistake. I had no idea abruptly stopping medications could make your emotions go up and down. What made it worse was the fact no one told me that would happen. So I started wondering what was wrong with me besides lupus. My doctors were great and stepped in to make sure I was back to 'normal.'

"Fortunately, I have an incredible family who has stood by me through everything. People always say that, but it's true. You really need to have a support system in place. Otherwise, how do you deal with changes in treatments, lupus flares and just life in general?

"I am lucky. My kidneys are working, my family is incredible, our friends are always there for me and I've been given a chance to go back to work. One of the things you learn is that with lupus you must make changes in your life. So, I am working—not at the same level I did, but I have a goal: To be able to retire and enjoy retirement.

"One of the best things I did after being diagnosed was call the Lupus International Support Center. I became connected and have made life-long friends. We support each other, because we get it. All we have to say is, 'It's another lupus day,' and we get it. Trying to help others will touch your own heart in ways you might not expect. By sharing your wisdom and experiences you will give someone the greatest gift—hope."

In short, share! Let your family and friends help you. And ask for help when you need it.
Sometimes people just don't know what they can do to make it better for you. Make friends with
other lupus patients. Once you do, you will understand how nice it is to just be able to say,
"I'm having a lupus moment," and have someone really understand on a whole other level.
Make sure you don't isolate yourself. Being with other people will make you feel better.
You won't feel so alone.

Getting over the loss of my husband and maintaining my health regimen to avoid more strokes and other setbacks, so I will be here for my children.

"JUST WHEN I WAS STARTING A NEW life with my late husband, Bobby Hatfield of the Righteous Brothers, it happened.

"I was lying on a Hawaiian beach, enjoying a day in the sun, and was suddenly covered with a rash. I itched from head to toe. It wasn't sunburn! How could this happen when I just moved from Chicago to sunny Newport Beach, California?

"Although I was diagnosed rather quickly, I did go back and forth for numerous tests, doctor visits and rechecks. At first it appeared that the lupus was under control, then out of nowhere, it reared its ugly head. There was a point when I was in a wheelchair, had slurred speech and couldn't get out of bed. My life looked bleak—especially when I read those early books on lupus that said I had as few as five years to live.

"Meanwhile, I was trying to plan a lifetime of happiness with my husband and was terrified I wouldn't live to enjoy it. We wanted to have children. Doctors said that would never happen. I defied the odds and had Vallyn and Dustin. The best I ever felt was when I was pregnant. I was also fortunate to find two doctors that made a world of difference in my life. I was able to walk on my own and begin living my life again.

"My husband and I realized we couldn't be the only ones facing the numerous problems of this almost unheard-of autoimmune disease, nor did we want anyone else to feel as alone as we did when we heard the diagnosis. We became adamant that something had to be done to find a cure, and that's when we created the Bobby Hatfield Charity Golf Classic. Hosting this event has introduced me to great people who support our cause, as well as lupus patients who are anxious for a cure. The golf classic gave Bobby and me a chance to make a difference in someone's life. You hear it all the time, but it's true—helping others really does help you.

"Luckily, Bobby and my family stood by me and kept me from sinking into depression during all the lows. My family and our golf fundraising project have been amazing medicine for me. They have made it possible for me to endure high doses of steroids, fatigue and related problems such as polynueropathy and strokes, to cope with the loss of Bobby and now to continue his legacy by carrying on the event we created."

If there are people who stress you out, avoid them. Don't let the unkindness of others get you down. You already have enough stress with your disease. Those people aren't worth it. You need to save your energy and strength to live as full a life as you can, and the only way you can do it is by focusing on the good things in life and the people who love you. And remember, it's okay to let others help you.

LINDA HATFIELD

DANIELLE CALLAS

I had to quit working and go on disability for six years, but through sheer determination I slowly built up my strength with the goal of working part-time. I decided to live through the pain, to take lots of fish oil to be healthier, and now I'm working full-time. It's still a constant battle. I also have MGUS, which is a form of bone marrow cancer, Hashimoto disease, high blood pressure and asthma.

I'm exhausted from my full-time job, so I rest on weekends and don't have much of a social life, but at the end of each workday I can say that I made a difference for each student I touched.

DANIELLE LOVES TO HELP YOUNG adults.

All of them.

Even the hard-crusted young man who had been a tough gang leader.

"Look at me. I'm sick and I drag myself to work every day. If I can be here and apply myself to be my best, so can you," she'd tell him, time and again.

He started listening. He came to her office for a pep talk when he was afraid he was slipping back. He came again when he felt cornered by the world and couldn't see a way out. He returned each time he needed a kick in the pants.

Today he is an art director for a major magazine. He emerged as an outstanding student at the Brooks Institute and a fine example of the host of teens and young adults who call Danielle Callas, "Mom." "I'm so proud of him. I love him dearly and cried for joy the day he graduated," she says of this bad boy turned achiever, under her tutelage.

Danielle cares about her flock of students. She gives them courage. She pushes and pulls them over the rough spots. She shows them that they can do it. "I tell them about working, in spite of lupus. I don't hold any punches. I tell them how difficult it has been for me.

"I thought I had the flu and it wouldn't go away," she says, describing her first lupus symptoms. "I took steroids, pain meds, rested a lot, but still couldn't get over the fatigue. Finally, my doctor tested my sed (sedimentation) rate, which measures inflammation, and I was diagnosed with lupus, which eventually affected my kidneys, liver and neurological system. I felt like I'd been given a death sentence and wondered if I'd ever be all right."

Danielle was born in Belgium and grew up in Canada. At a still-wet-behind-the-ears age, she was accepted as the first nine-year-old to be a student at L'ecole des Beaux Arts University in Canada.

Her parents were firm about their children being good students. "My parents told me that I had to learn my times tables by Christmas, or no Christmas present for me. Well, I didn't master times tables and received no Christmas present. It was a hard lesson that I never forgot. That experience taught me to work harder, to stretch myself and to try, try again. Once a student at Brooks, she's now the Department Chairwoman of Graphic Design and Multimedia.

Arriving in the United States at sixteen, she fell in love, married and is an enthusiastic mom of two fine young men.

"Unfortunately my marriage didn't last, but being a mom is forever. I'm so proud of my children."

Have the attitude that it's good to be alive. Pretend like you're normal and don't allow negativity to rule your life. And do things you enjoy. For instance, I still do freelance illustrations for books. I always tell my students, "You are here to learn the basics. It's up to you to take your dreams as far as you want. No one can stop you. Only you are in charge of your life. So go for it and don't let any illness or friends get in the way. You can do it!"

Besides having lupus, I've been diagnosed with fibromyalgia. The fatigue can be so strong that I've been bedridden for months. Listen to your body. If you are tired, take a nap, more than one if need be. It's okay if you need to slow down. Like many others, I also experience "lupus fog," so I try to keep my mind active by beading jewelry. It's important to keep looking for solutions.

"I WAS HIT WITH HUMILITY IN 1986 when finally diagnosed with lupus. Until then I was busy working for an Illinois department store, spotting fashion trends and putting them on the runway. Lupus humbled me because it changed my perspective on life and my faith.

"I hadn't felt good since 1974 and doctors questioned the possibility of lupus or leukemia. I had symptoms that could have gone either way—low white blood cell count, fatigue, mouth ulcers, a rocking type of pain, then inflamed lungs, headaches and stomach pain. The tests just couldn't confirm either. Finally, after three major surgeries and several hospital stays that required isolation, I tested positive for lupus.

"For twelve years I worked really hard at balancing a career and family. During this time I had lupus, but had not been diagnosed yet. At the height of my career I was the Vice President Fashion Merchandising Director for twenty-six stores. I traveled to New York one week every month. I had no idea lupus was the reason for my fatigue. It took every ounce of energy I had to have my career and be a wife and mother. My husband and children were and still are my first priority. It was really tough on them having a wife and mom who was so sick.

"To this day, my faith grows. I have learned to let go. Possibly one of the best antidotes is finding humor in things that might not seem too funny. Laughter really can be the best medicine. You have to first accept your limitations, then make adjustments and be able to still have fun. Fun might come in different packages. Just because you have lupus doesn't mean you should stop living.

"Sometimes the hardest thing to do is to get out of yourself and help others. I know it is hard for some to imagine not feeling well and still being able to be there for someone else. I didn't realize how much it would make a difference in my own life until I tried it. Going to support groups and serving on the Lupus International board and committees has given me a gift—helping others really has helped me. I actually feel better after I help others. We all have our ups and downs, but it's what you do with them that counts. Positive thoughts will extend back to you. Give it a try and see for yourself."

Get a heating pad, pain medications and a hobby . . . and also a strong husband, who, in my case, has had to pick up all the beads I drop! Now, on a more serious note, support groups can change your life. A spiritual and holistic approach to health, such as chanting, meditation, reflexology and acupuncture, may work for you.

CINDY PUJAYANA

It's maintaining a comfortable level with my body, getting enough sleep, eating healthy food, exercising and taking my meds—while attending college to become a teacher. And, because I've had problems with my kidneys and numerous other complications, including pneumonia, glaucoma and a hip replacement, I've had intravenous steroids and chemotherapy. This causes me to be unsure about being able to have a family.

"'DO YOU WANT TO STAY IN THE United States or do you want to go back to Indonesia?' my parents asked me when I was four years old. They had recently enjoyed an extended stay in the U.S., visiting from our Indonesian homeland.

"I thought and thought.

"Disneyland was in the United States and not in Indonesia.

"'The United States,' I confidently answered.

"My seven-year-old brother agreed.

"We stayed.

"To this day I marvel that my parents were so thoughtful of our opinions that they considered the desires of such little children when making a monumental decision. But then, that typifies my parents. And none of us have regrets.

"I was always an artist. Even when I was a little girl, teachers would ask me to be the one to make the poster or banner. I always added detail. Even today, besides loving to paint, I love to bake. I try to add a special look to everything I prepare. After all, I'm serving my family and friends, and I want what I cook to be pleasing in looks and taste.

"I was a very happy child, kind of a tomboy," she laughs. "I loved gymnastics and was pretty good at it. My brother was my favorite playmate. He taught me how to ride my bike and skateboard. My dad was always ready to capture the moment with his camera. My mother was and is my great inspiration. Her unconditional love and support shaped my life. She is my steadfast and loving friend, who gives continuously and without reserve. She is an excellent role model for my life."

An art student at Pitzer College, Cindy is making up for lost time these days. There were those tough years when lupus almost took her life. She's not in remission, but enjoys a manageable period that allows her to attend college, paint unabashedly and take salsa-dancing lessons with her boyfriend.

At twenty-seven, Cindy still lives at home with a nurturing family. She dreams of having her own family some day.

"I was seventeen and a high school senior when I started getting achy and having a constant fever, followed by fatigue and the malar (butterfly) rash on my face. I started getting mouth and nose sores, my joints ached and my hair fell out. I felt moody and irritable and really depressed . . . and many of my friends became apprehensive and didn't come over to visit me. Even my family couldn't understand my fatigue and depression. I felt like I was dying." Finally one doctor speculated, "This looks like some kind of lupus." It was.

"I started Prednisone. Immediate side effects included weight gain, water retention and moon face. I felt grotesque, handicapped. I no longer looked like the girl elected homecoming queen just a few months before.

"Difficulties continued, while I struggled to have a life. While everyone was anxious over the Y2K crisis, I had an emergency of my own: kidney failure. After many treatments of chemotherapy, my body limped back to a better degree of kidney function. Then I had another crisis: bilateral avascular necrosis of the hips. I realized I needed to find doctors who specialized in lupus and could provide better treatments. With knowledgable doctors and more appropriate treatments, I feel in control.

"There are still some days when all I can do is rise out of bed, perhaps read a book or do easy things around the house. Better, though, are the days when I feel I can accomplish anything. I have the energy and stamina to drive places, to dance for hours into the night and to help my family and friends."

Listen to your body and slow down if you need to. Don't think you need to take on the world. I have found some things that make me happy within my limits, but I had to work up to them. I'd also advise newly diagnosed patients to surround themselves with positive, supportive people.

I am fatigued often and can only do one or two tasks a day. My hip has been replaced and my knee is about to be replaced. I am not able to resume my career, which I'd love to do, and my memory stinks. I'm still looking for keys I misplaced last year.

RICK IS ON A MISSION. IT'S NOT HIS first. The United States Air Force enjoyed his enthusiastic services until he retired with the rank of Master Sergeant, the highest rank one can achieve as a non-commissioned officer. "I loved the Air Force and I love my country," he lets you know right off.

Then, he "went Hollywood" and served vital roles as the purchasing director and then the post-production engineer for MGM Studios and Consolidated Film Industries. "Lupus got in the way, or I'd still be there," he declares.

The most important mission, aside from nurturing his family, is his current one: Lupus awareness. He would shout from the rooftop, to let people know about lupus and the need for a cure, if he could climb up there. But no matter—his voice is heard.

He's not a man to mince his words. "It's a wonder I grew up intact. I was adventurous and tried everything that looked like fun. I tried those old roller skates, the type that you put on your shoes and tightened with a key. I fell down constantly, skinning my ankles, knees and elbows. I tried the original skateboards when they came out. More scrapes and bruises. I can't count the number of times I fell off my bike. I totally enjoyed Little League. When I was older, I was a pretty good volleyball player. Since I'm short, I was the set-up guy for a two-man volleyball team. We played in a Southern California league.

"I was first diagnosed in 1992, soon after my father's death. I came down with flu-like symptoms and, after ten days in the hospital, was told I had lupus. I thought it was a disease women got, but learned it also can strike men. I had more lupus flares that sent me to the hospital and then had a seizure that lasted nearly five days and began to cause brain damage. To stop the seizure, I was placed into a coma for six weeks and then brought out of it slowly. I had to relearn how to talk, walk and even eat. Worst of all, I didn't even know my family—and I have a beautiful wife and daughter. But I've recovered and haven't had another episode, although my life has greatly changed."

I know you hear a lot of people talking about faith, but it's true for me. Seeking the Lord gives me strength. I love to travel, so taking small trips help fill that passion and make me feel normal. By the way, always talk to your doctor about your travel plans. Cruises and visits to third-world countries can be dangerous for lupus patients. And stay focused on hobbies, especially if you are primarily housebound. If you can, spread the word about lupus. I take posters of upcoming fundraisers to businesses around my community.

RICK KAHLE

STEPHANIE MIDDLETON

I can no longer work at any job because of my many chronic conditions. I spend my energy on trying to feel better, not being mad at what I lost or can't do. Focus on what's in front of you and what you can do for yourself.

SHE GREETS YOU WITH A WARM SMILE and a hello. You are the center of her attention. Her story is a story of courage and strength. She is honest and forthright about her life.

Stephanie was raised in the Church of Christ and was raised to have a strong spiritual sense and to have trust and faith in God. Ask her how she keeps her positive outlook on life—she'll tell you it is her faith.

"I was thirty-six years old when I was involved in a car accident which caused a large hematoma on the left side of my head. I continued to feel ill for the next eight months. Doctors didn't know what was wrong. More symptoms followed—headaches, hair loss, fatigue, weight loss, anemia, loss of appetite, fevers, lost most of the vision in my right eye and had two seizures. After many tests were run, the doctors learned that I had five bleeding lesions on the brain. I came home from the hospital suffering from paralysis on the left side, headaches, double vision, severe fatigue and depression. But I never gave up. I was determined to get well and get back to work.

"I grew up believing in God and that he is all-powerful. I know that the mind of God is not like the mind of man. I didn't get mad at God because I had lupus, but was upset with him that I was so sick. It truly was hard to understand this. It took years and years to get to where I am today with my faith. I've learned that no matter how small, you have to count the blessings you have.

"My oldest sister came to my apartment every day, bringing help and moral support. I will be forever grateful to her for helping me at a time when I could do very little for myself.

"The key to me is not to worry about something that I can't change, but to pray about it. I've learned not to dwell on it. Lupus is *not* a death sentence.

"I attend support groups and find they really do help. Admittedly my first meeting sent me home in tears for fear of what could happen. I knew there was a group for me so I kept going. I found one and with it came friendship, compassion and tools to learn about my condition."

Today Stephanie shows no signs of the terrific struggle just described; a tribute to her remarkable character and her faith. However, she still does have days where she suffers from fatigue, anemia, and swollen legs and feet. The obvious thing one learns about Stephanie is that she is a very strong person, and compassionate where people are concerned.

Don't expect everyone to understand lupus and all its symptoms. It's hard not to, but don't take it personally.

I try to be independent as much as I can possibly be, but I know when I have to depend on others to help me, and I don't let pride get in the way.

I've been single all my life and enjoy it very much. When I was in my twenties, thirties and forties, I thought I should be trying to find that someone special, and that would lead to marriage. That's what society has taught women to think. If you are not married by a certain age you are considered to be an old maid or biddy. I can only guess that it would be nice to be married if the right gentleman came along. But in the meantime, I can honestly say that I truly try to enjoy each moment of life.

Because of joint pain and tremors, I worry about dropping things, but the daily challenge is just getting out of bed and walking out the door. I don't think I could do it, if it weren't for my faith in God. I want to be able to help lupus patients deal with their disease and the depression that goes with it.

"WHEN I BECAME ILL, I WAS SO MAD at God. I didn't know what to do.

"Why me?

"What was this illness that gave me fatigue, anemia and pain in my legs? I was just a teenager, for heaven's sake.

"I had been raised to believe in God and to pray. An answer didn't seem to come. I couldn't understand why I wasn't getting better.

"Then an answer did come. My cousin came and spoke to me. She suffers from multiple sclerosis and is the most religious person I have ever met. Despite her illness, she goes to work everyday as a pharmacist and thanks God for each breath she takes. She inspired me to become closer to God even though, at the time, I didn't have a diagnosis. I now know that I will have a life-long struggle, but I am now convinced that God will help me conquer it.

"At twenty-one, I now realize that I have been blessed by having the best family that I could have ever wanted. My parents encourage me to be successful, despite my ailments. I have a wonderful brother. He and I are very close.

"My grandfather demonstrated the importance of continuous love and support and was the best role model. I can still see him, wearing worn slacks and always the same jacket. He didn't like to buy new things. He took every opportunity to teach me about life. He always put our needs above his needs. I miss my Gramps and treasure the necklace that he wore every day. Grandma gave it to me. 'That's my *mija* (girl),' he would always say about me. I was his pride and joy."

A psychology major at Ventura Community College, Karena resides with her family. "I can help those who feel lost due to the discrimination in this chaotic world toward the chronically and mentally ill. I want to work in a medical setting where I'm helping a young population. I want to be known as a person who helps others in need," Karena says with spirited conviction.

"I was always getting the flu and other illnesses more than anybody else in my family, but then I started getting constant fatigue, iron-deficiency anemia and pain in my legs. Four years later, on June 6, 2004, I was finally diagnosed with lupus. I'm on steroids, Imuran and Methotrexate plus other drugs, but I still get a bronchial infection at least once a month. The disease also has affected my central nervous system, causing several types of tremor and vascular problems in my hands. Yet, I'm fortunate to have good doctors, my religious faith and a very caring family."

You may think when you are a teenager that you are invincible—but you're not. It's a lie. So, if you've been diagnosed with lupus, forget about vanity and be safe. Whenever you're outside in the sunlight, wear sunscreen and protective clothing so the sun won't flare up your disease. Another thing: don't be afraid of all the blood tests and other diagnostic procedures you will have. If you've already tolerated the pain of lupus, you'll be able to endure anything.

KARENA NICOLE MARTINEZ

My first challenge was being told I could not have children, but I did. Then it was being pregnant with my first child and learning I had avascular necrosis (dead bone) in both hips and having surgery. Then there was a forty-five-pound weight gain from a major flare-up after the September 11, 2001, tragedy, followed by the death of my dad on September 12.

Today, I'd say my greatest challenges are staying as healthy as I can and being available to nurture my family.

"THE VALUE OF HAVING A SPECIAL friend developed early in my life. When I was a little girl, maybe four or five years old, I had a neighbor named Isabelle, who allowed me to call her Aunt Isa. I helped her in her gardens, trimming the flowers, picking up weeds and dead flowers, cleaning the birdbaths. As payment for my work, I could pick out a bone china teacup and saucer to have coffee with Aunt Isa. My coffee was a teaspoon of coffee and the rest milk. Sitting in her kitchen and looking out at her beautiful garden, I learned to appreciate nature and fine things and to love and respect older people.

"Again, years later when I was devastated by my parents' divorce, I had a friend whose mom, Freda, listened to me. My mom is an angel on earth, but when I was sixteen, we were not so close. Freda would tell me things like, 'JoAnne, you have two choices in life: Be less than you are or be more than you are.' I remember that so clearly. I went on to graduate from high school one-and-a-half years earlier than my class and then to become a self-taught accountant. I learned I could depend on myself no matter what and that I could take care of myself. I have Freda to thank for that. She and I remained close friends until her death in 2001. Today, my mom is my biggest supporter, friend and mentor, for whom I am always grateful and thankful.

"I have many wonderful friends today, and feel honored to be surrounded by such a strong circle of support. For them I am thankful. My very best friend and life partner is my husband John. He and I were told that we might not be able to have children, but we beat the odds and now have two wonderful children, Jenna and John J. (J.J.), who are the center of our world."

JoAnne is filled with nonstop energy. Lupus and multiple hip surgeries have not slowed her down. It is as if she believes that if she sits down, she won't be able to get up, so she keeps going.

As the former co-facilitator of the Conejo Valley lupus support group, she constantly found inspiring guest speakers for monthly meetings. She drove people to doctors' appointments, held their hands when they were scared and helped them fill out papers for Social Security.

"An early lupus symptom was stiffness in my fingers. I couldn't type or throw a bowling ball. At first, I thought I was just over-working. Then I thought I might have arthritis or carpal tunnel syndrome. In June 1994, I was diagnosed with SLE. It was organ-threatening, mostly affecting my kidneys—lupus nephritis and also cutaneous (discoid) lupus. My hips have been greatly affected, and this year I had my sixth hip replacement."

Go out and get every book on the subject of lupus. Keep a diary and check the Internet for news on lupus drugs and therapies so you can talk to your doctor more intelligently about the pros and cons of drugs for you. And don't wait too long to see your doctor about any health problems. Finally, participate in life, but learn your triggers and/or limits. There is no magic pill. Making it better is all in your attitude.

There are so many! In a single month, I may make a dozen visits to the UCLA Medical Center to see numerous doctors, plus endure myriad tests ranging from blood tests to biopsies. I also take at least thirty medications a day and constantly have to defend my need for them to my insurance companies.

There's an inner battle, too. I push myself to find humor in my disabilities and steroid-enlarged body. I may not feel perky, but I "do" perky, and, honestly, I sometimes convince even myself.

"I SPENT MOST OF MY LIFE TRYING TO be perfect and make everybody like me. I never slowed down because I might run out of time to achieve all I could be. I was Little Red Riding Hood running from the wolf loping behind me.

"There were perfect moments in my life—my wedding day on a sunny veranda, the birth of my daughter Scarlett, my two trips to New York to accept Aldo awards for fashion writing and lots of little pleasures with family and friends.

"Growing up in Los Angeles, I won my first writing contest at the age of nine, and my prize was a camera. From there, I followed my passion for writing and later for photography.

"After college, I landed my first newspaper job in the desert town of Ridgecrest, California. There, I was given creative freedom and discovered I excelled at fashion layouts—and that I could have fun on the job and still win awards. It was my starting point on the fashion fast track, and I stopped looking over my shoulder for that wolf.

"When my family and I moved back to Los Angeles, I worked at *The Daily Breeze* newspaper in Torrance and for thirteen years at the *Los Angeles Daily News* in the San Fernando Valley. I worked the red carpet at the Oscars and had a Rolodex filled with names like Mr. Blackwell, Max Azria of BCBG, Nicole Miller, Tommy Hilfiger, Valentino, David Dart and Bob Mackie. My all-time favorite story was a makeover I did on the late comedian Rodney Dangerfield, which was televised on the entertainment news show *Extra*.

"I was so busy with my job and family that when I stumbled and actually met the wolf at the door—lupus—I thought my life was over.

"I'd had several bouts of pneumonia and then suffered from what I thought was a food allergy that caused edema and rashes. But a skilled allergist knew it was something more serious. After he diagnosed me with lupus, I was stunned. I asked my husband to look up this mystery disease on the Internet. Bad news. I could expect to live only five years more.

"But I was too tough to admit defeat. Even when I became bedridden for several months because of sores on my legs and fluid in my hips, I begged my rheumatologist to get me back on my feet and back to work. He did, but he couldn't stop the assortment of conditions that changed my life forever.

"The wolf may think he's won. But lupus forced me to slow down and realize that life isn't about perfection. It took awhile, but I've learned that some people will never like you. And that you can still look attractive wearing a larger size because beauty comes from within.

"Although I was able to work for two years after my diagnosis, lupus took its toll and I retired from the job I loved. Now that I have more free time, I have reestablished old friendships, made new ones, written a book and even tried my hand at neighborhood politics.

"I thank God for my husband Don, who is my rock. He helped me accept who I was and who I am today. My mother Irene has always been my role model and cheerleader, and, with two daughters and two grandsons, I am lucky to have had a full life."

Remember that this disease has highs and lows, so enjoy the good days with friends and family and take care of yourself on the others. Work harder than you did in the past to keep yourself well-groomed. Small efforts, such as dressing in monochromatic color schemes with a scoop-neck tank top and eye-catching accessories, can make you like what you see in the mirror. People will notice your new fashion stance instead of your cane, wig or rash. Honest, it works!

BARBARA DE WITT

Well, the joint pain and the stiffness can be pretty bad. The more a joint hurts, the more I need to move it, so I get up early to walk a few miles. Also, juggling a career, motherhood and married life can be a challenge even for the healthiest of women.

"I HAVE NEVER BEEN ONE TO LIE down and be sick. I liked to be outdoors playing with my friends. I spent hours practicing cartwheels, ice-skating and playing kick ball (to the dismay of my family). For the most part, my grandmother and my Aunt Liz raised me. They had reason to worry about me, though.

"By the time I was four, I had lost all range of motion in my left wrist. As I grew, the lack of use of that arm caused it to atrophy, a fact I kept hidden from my friends for years by wearing long sleeves, even in the summer.

"My treatments started when I turned eight years old. The doctors at Childrens Hospital Los Angeles tried injecting my wrist with cortisone. To this day I have a rather large scar on my left wrist, and it still hurts when I think about that shot. Upon requesting copies of my childhood records, I was surprised that doctors considered SLE, as my original diagnosis was Juvenile Rheumatoid Arthritis (JRA).

"I spent a lot of time in physical therapy as a child, yet don't recall a lot of pain. My grandmother and my Aunt Liz taught me how to focus my energy on more positive experiences. My grandmother taught me that no matter what life throws at me, I must press forward.

"I carry that discipline with me today. I wake up with pain, stiffness and lethargy, but try not to complain. I practice martial arts twice a week and participate in 5Ks whenever possible. I am a mother and a wife, and I work full time. People are surprised when they find out I have lupus.

"I was diagnosed when I was twenty-five. I felt extremely tired and experienced severe joint pain. One day, I fell asleep in my car at work during lunch, and a colleague woke me. Home from work, I felt worse. I felt as though my veins were on fire, and I couldn't sit still. I blacked out and my husband rushed me to the hospital. I didn't respond to antibiotics, so the doctors tried steroids and I improved. I had cortisone shots in several joints, and both my knees were drained, repeatedly.

"I also have lupus related anemia and Raynaud's phenomenon. Fortunately, I am stable on Plaquenil now and have resumed working full time.

"I jokingly tell people that I refuse to be sick and that is why I look so healthy. Recently, however, x-rays of my arms and hands revealed that my right arm appeared solid and strong whereas my left arm looked virtually transparent and brittle. The reality of my condition was evident. As much as I try to look solid, I am not. After that appointment, I sat in my car and cried. As I thought about it, I realized the comparison of my arms was my rheumatologist's way of communicating to me the importance of accepting that I do have lupus and that I must be careful.

"I have a blessed life, with a caring, supportive family. My grandmother's spirit still guides me today, though she died in 1993. My wonderful husband is protective of me and understands my desire to be healthy.

"My daughter Keeva is active in Tae Kwon Do, swim classes, ballet and tap, and enjoys kindergarten. Keeva does not know, yet, that I have lupus. Why should she? It's a very small part of who I am. I want her to see me as being healthy and strong."

Just because lupus is a terminal illness doesn't mean you have been handed a death sentence. All it means is that there is no cure for it yet. It is important to be disciplined enough to keep yourself healthy. I firmly believe that one should eat right, exercise regularly, get plenty of rest, not stress about things and enjoy life. That is how I stay in remission.

Trying to keep my health in check with proper rest and medical care; traveling and other things I once enjoyed now exhaust me, I pace myself and know that there are trade offs, enjoying a day out with my children may mean two days of bed rest in return. Personal hygiene, housework, and day-to-day responsibilities are more than just normal chores—they are monumental. My husband and children keep me motivated to get up, move and want to feel better. My parents are a source of constant support.

"FAITH AND FAMILY. THESE ARE what I owe to getting me through the difficult times and the daily struggles I face each day with lupus. The need for something to get me through the extreme ups, downs and most of all the not knowing of what may come next. I am blessed to have a dedicated and supportive husband and family.

"The need to know why I hadn't felt well and was getting sicker and the desperation to put a name and an end to it was there. I knew something was wrong, but had no idea it would be lupus. I was diagnosed after I gave birth to our first daughter when I was thirty-one. This was supposed to be the happiest time of my life and I ended up being too sick and weak to care for my baby and even myself.

"Finally, my gastroenterologist was the only doctor to consider running the blood panel for lupus. It came back positive for SLE. The next morning my husband and I met with a rheumatologist. And this started our journey, among some of the more disturbing things the doctor told us was that I wouldn't have any more children—but I did, another girl! What a gift.

"As time goes on the more health issues and challenges arise—chronic pain and fatigue, muscle aches, asthma, lupus arthritis, discoid lupus, colitis, pleurisy, cataracts, blood clot, peritonitis, gangrene in my intestines, sepsis, medication side effects, degenerative disc disease in my back. One of the more difficult times has been recovering from back surgery, both the mental and physical aspects. There always seems to be something. But even with all of the pain, fatigue and lifestyle changes, I keep the faith and hope for my future in focus with my support circle and pro-active medical care.

"When something new happens it helps to remember that you have been through a great deal already and that the strength is there to handle one more thing. Even when you think you can't, you have to believe you can do it. Surround yourself with loving, supportive friends and family. Join a support group! It really makes a world of difference. Just knowing you can count on them is a relief and takes away some of the burden. It might have been easier to have given up but I chose to do a little at a time and I am proud of my accomplishments. After my back surgery, the motivation to never go through that again was enough to motivate me to start a diet and exercise program and lose the fifty pounds gained from being on steroids. When I meet new people who have this disease my heart goes out to them, because I get what it means. I let them know if they need help I will be there for them. Kindness and love go a long way."

Accept that among the devastating effects of lupus, lupus is the ultimate look good disease and people do not realize or sympathize that you are really sick because they cannot see it. Use the disability placard, leave events early, and learn to just say no! Join a lupus support group! Without a doubt after the initial diagnosis these support groups not only educated me and my family, they gave us hope. I really like this saying, "Life is not measured by the number of breaths we take, but by the moments that take our breath away."

CATHERINE CAPALDI

LISAJO McGEE

I don't want to feel useless, or be useless. One of the toughest things you face, as a side effect of being a kid with lupus, is that you end up being dependent on others when you are desperately trying to gain your independence. I have learned to do volunteer work when I feel well, and as an adult, I am proud of that track record.

"WHEN I LOST MY HAIR AND WAS A completely bald teenager, I concentrated on growing six inches of hair in three years or less. I did it! Plus, in the meantime, I got to wear really cool wigs, and I must say I stood out in my crowd of friends.

"I was diagnosed at age fifteen and spent seventy-five percent of that first year in the hospital—including my sixteenth birthday. I guess you could say I have experienced it all. I had staph infections, a stroke, a brain aneurysm, lupus nephritis, scarring of my face, chemo-fried hair and hip replacements.

"You know, being sick as a kid, you don't know any different, so you learn to adapt. Yes, it's hard—harder than hard. Lupus really can rob you of your dignity. You have to *make* yourself bounce back. And I wasn't about to give in to the unkind people who teased me about my appearance. Although, honestly, people can be really mean. Not just kids, but adults too. Try not to let it get you down. Surround yourself with people who genuinely care about you. Let them know how you are feeling and that you are having a tough time.

"I think young people with lupus need to realize that they too can dream. I realized that it was important to set goals and strive to achieve them. My time frame may be a little off, but I'm not giving up on my dreams. For instance, I thought it would be cool to be a private investigator. I now have my license (but haven't actually worked as one—yet).

"I'm energized by knowing that people depend on me. I volunteer at high schools and the local Kiwanis Club, send books to soldiers, read to senior citizens, plant trees in fire-burned areas and write a newsletter for the Malibu Senior Center. Also I'm working on the Cruisin' the Canyon benefit for Lupus International."

In general, young patients should research their disease and be informed. Don't just let it happen to you. Be the captain of your team. Ask questions and find out why you have to take certain medications. (After having thirteen hip replacements, I now know enough to ask about everything.) Parents, you should be supportive, but beware that excessive coddling can sometimes drive a teen nuts!

My life revolves around my doctor appointments and dealing with ordinary things in life, like trying to comb my hair, getting in and out of the bathtub and dressing, because my hands are always swollen.

"WARM, FRIENDLY AND SUPPORTIVE. That is how I try to be with everyone. You can change a person's day with something as simple as a smile. No matter what circumstances you are in, there has to be something good you can take from it. In my case, I feel blessed that lupus has not affected my kidneys, liver or heart. Sometimes you may have to dig deep to find even the smallest thing that is okay, but keep digging—you'll find it.

"If I didn't keep a positive attitude, I never would have graduated from college. Not only do I have lupus, but Raynaud's phenomenon and fibromyalgia too. Just like you, I have my good days and bad. On the bad ones, I need to keep in mind that good ones will follow.

"Lupus didn't strike me in the ways I've heard or read about. My first unusual symptom was terrible stomach cramps that were so severe that my office called an ambulance. At first the doctors thought I might have a cervical infection, but then it went away.

"A few years later I had muscle spasms and pain in my hands and arms, which affected my ability to work. Then I was diagnosed with lupus. My most dramatic event occurred right after I had an upper gastrointestinal exam. I kept feeling dizzy and sick but went home and then woke up at two in the morning, vomiting blood. I blacked out and found myself on the floor, face down in the planter near the bed! My kids called 911 and I spent three days in the hospital and received five pints of blood. It turned out to be a lupus-related anemia, which has required me to have a port-a-cath implanted above my right breast so the doctors make it easier for blood and iron treatments to be administered.

"I have found that you just can't predict what lupus will do next. Each person is different. Every flare is different. Understanding how to live with this disease takes time. Successfully living with it means you must have a support network in place—family, friends, co-workers and a support group. That's why I am always trying to spread the word about lupus, along with suggestions on how to handle the symptoms and treatments. I want to help everyone I can. People need to know that, if left untreated, it can get worse."

Have a network of family and friends who will help you when you need it, but don't let them make an invalid of you. Spouses and friends need to be patient with you because you can't do what you did before. I also advise newly diagnosed people to apply for Social Security benefits and not give up if you are turned down on the first attempt. It took me three times before I got approved. And when you are feeling better, try supporting others with lupus to let them know that there is still a lot of living to do.

SYBIL JOHNSON

Recently, I've had a lot of neck and back pain and have gone to physical therapy several times a week. The therapy, with the exercises I do at home, have really helped. I know you just naturally slow down as you age, regardless of an illness. So, I just take things in stride.

"WE LIVED ON THE THIRD FLOOR OF a mortuary from the time I was five until I was seventeen. So, I can honestly say that I lived at death's door for many years."

Rosalie's lifestyle, and the funeral jokes associated with it, often delighted friends. But when there was a funeral or a family of the deceased was there, friends couldn't come in and she had to be really quiet, she recalls.

It was lonely, being an only child, but her best friend came from a family of six children, and through her, Rosalie says she came to know what being a part of a family meant. And it prepared her for the rest of her life.

"When I was eleven, walking home as usual from school, I saw mother sitting on the steps of a meeting hall that I always passed. I was frightened that something bad had happened as she hurried over to me. But it was wonderful news. She was going to have a baby!

"My sister was born the following December and came home on Christmas Eve. What a great present! I finally had a sibling. Christmas has always been my favorite holiday and her birth made it even more special."

Rosalie found out in later years that her mother had had over a dozen miscarriages, attempting to have another child. Doctors never knew why, but looking back, Rosalie believes it must have been fibromyalgia.

"My husband of forty-three years is a jewel. Frank was my first husband's best friend and was there to support me and our infant son when my first husband died in a tragic accident. We had our daughter together and now have nine grandchildren, plus seven foster grandchildren. I have been truly blessed in my life.

"Unlike many of the young women today who are quickly diagnosed with lupus, it took many years of fatigue, flu-like symptoms, Raynaud's phenomenon, Sjogren's Syndrome and depression before I was finally diagnosed in 1987. Part of the reason it took so long was lack of information about lupus by many primary care doctors. After I went on a cruise to Mexico and got a terrible rash and flare, it was clear that I needed help. I wrote down all the symptoms (no matter how trivial I thought they were) and saw a new doctor. I presented the list and asked if it meant anything. He said it did.

"Finally, I had blood tests that proved I wasn't imagining anything. I was immediately seen by a rheumatologist who discovered I also had fibromyalgia, thyroid problems, chronic inflammation of my digestive tract and constant stomach pain. I was put on steroids for a short time, but I feel the Plaquenil, Prilosec and thyroid medicine have kept my disease, as well as my weight, under control."

Especially if you are older or have bone problems, you've got to stretch your muscles to strengthen them and relieve pain and to try other exercises to promote bone growth. But don't dwell on the exercises you can't do, just do what you can. And then focus on one project a day, whether it's a load of laundry, making phone calls or spending the day with your grandchildren. On special occasions, like Christmas, go ahead and wear yourself out a little. It'll be worth it.

*Courage was
never designed
for show;*

It isn't a thing that can come and go . . . .

—EDGAR A. GUEST

CHAPTER 2

WHY NO TWO PATIENTS ARE ALIKE

Our imagination is the only limit

to what we can hope to have in the future.

—CHARLES F. KETTERING

INTRODUCTION

A PHYSICIAN'S TRANSLATION *of* SYMPTOMS AND CONDITIONS

*Y*ou've just heard from admirable people who are facing lupus with courage. They represent the diversity of lupus patients, and as different as they and their symptoms and accompanying diseases are, so too are the treatments.

In all of medicine, physicians learn that no two cases are alike. Even if the diagnostic label is similar.

There is no condition where this is more obvious than SLE.

The severity of the condition varies greatly from a mild form with, for example, a few skin lesions and painless mouth sores, to a life-threatening form with, for example, seizures and kidney failure. No two lupus cases are alike, and repeat flares among the same patient are not necessarily alike.

I use a buffet table analogy to explain differences among patients and among flares in the same individual. At a real buffet table, of course, it's usually all food and appealing items. With lupus, there's a vast array of items, but they are all undesirable. Instead of the patient choosing which manifestations they can live with, lupus decides how it will affect each patient. Some will get more of one item, skip others or get a little or a lot of all of them.

Among the variety of conditions and disorders lupus patients are subjected to are rashes, mouth sores, kidney disease, blood count abnormalities, seizures and arthritis. The list goes on and on. Some patients may only get one or two of these, while others will suffer from a little bit of everything.

The patient ultimately gets treated and hopefully goes into remission. Months to years later, the patient may have a recurrent flare of the disease. Analogous to someone going through a buffet line for a second time, patients may get exactly the same thing they experienced the first time in terms of quantities and types of symptoms, or they could end up with something completely different. Thus, as physicians, we cannot be too dependent upon recurrence of patterns in diagnosing and treating patients.

Lupus also has the ability to cause a huge variety of manifestations. Granted that some findings are more common, but the disease can run the gamut of medical pathology. There are innumerable different skin, lung, neurological and other body system findings that can occur. The problem is that lupus can mimic other processes such as infections. Simplistically, many lupus physicians use the philosophy that SLE can cause anything, but one has to rule out all other causes (such as infection, drug effects, toxins or atherosclerosis) before attributing the particular manifestation to lupus.

We have to convey to our patients that just because they carry a diagnosis of SLE and they have a new symptom, the new symptom may actually not be due to their SLE. Patience in making the proper diagnosis is of the utmost importance in choosing therapy that can make a life-saving difference.

One of the hardest aspects to accept when a patient has lupus is the unpredictable nature of the condition. An initial presenting flare may respond beautifully to therapy and go into remission— or not.

Remission in lupus is defined as relatively few symptoms while *still* on medication. While many patients are able to reach remission, not every patient gets a complete response to therapy. The strategy of most rheumatologists is to adequately treat the flare and then, when it's safe, back off the medications to minimize drug toxicity.

Caring for patients with lupus includes technical, therapeutic and psychosocial challenges. Technically, SLE and its manifestations can be difficult to diagnose. Therapeutically, there is a fine line between effectively treating the disease manifestations and successfully avoiding medication side effects. Psychosocially, one tries to comfort patients and family, provide support and encouragement in the battle against this terrible disease and convince them that this battle can indeed be won.

We cannot treat in advance. We do not have any sort of crystal ball that can adequately predict a disease flare. Potential toxicities of medications prevent us from treating before a manifestation occurs. Some patients may never have a recurrent flare; others may have many flares, some mild, others life-threatening. Yet doctors cannot justify giving cytoxan chemotherapy to a patient in remission who has never had kidney disease, just to make sure they don't get kidney disease in the future. Many researchers are actively working on methods to identify and predict who will get the different manifestations, hopefully allowing us to better treat quickly and safely.

One of the most difficult symptoms to treat in lupus patients is the fatigue or lack of energy. It can be frustrating to patients that we, as physicians, will tell them that they are in remission, yet they feel overwhelmingly exhausted. While we have great tools to treat rashes, pleurisy, arthritis, low blood counts and kidney disease, we have very little to help with fatigue. While some drugs such as hydroxychloroquine, quinacrine and DHEA may help a little with energy, the benefit is partial at best. Thus, we need to be supportive as possible, emphasizing proper rest and exercise, if feasible.

Perhaps the most important job of the physician treating lupus is to cultivate understanding and support of the patient's family and friends for the fight against the disease. Severe illness puts an obvious strain on a marriage. With lupus, the situation is compounded by the chronic nature of the condition. A spouse who is quite supportive initially may have some difficulty five or ten years later.

Sometimes patients may not outwardly appear ill, yet they still feel terrible. One needs to convey to families and friends that this is actually quite common and to encourage them do their best to sympathize and be there for support.

Finally, we need to instill the sense of optimism in the patients, spouses, families and friends, as well as other members of the medical community. This is not a false sense of optimism. We already have many great drugs to control the disease and resulting afflictions.

The predicted lifespan of a lupus patient is rapidly approaching the predicted lifespan of someone without lupus. There is literally an explosion of new knowledge and great new drugs on the horizon. These medications will have greater efficacy and less toxicity. They will be available in the not too distant future.

Things will indeed get better soon.

DAVID KLASHMAN, M.D.
Fellow, American College of Rheumatology
Associate Clinical Professor, UCLA School of Medicine
Private Practice, Arthritis Treatment Center, Torrance, California

What lies before us and what lies beyond are tiny

*compared to what
lies within us.*

—HENRY DAVID THOREAU

OKAY, NOW WHAT?

THE WISDOM *of* LIVING WITH LUPUS

You're sick and are now wondering what you are going to do for the rest of your life. Are you ever going to feel better? Will you be able to fulfill your dreams? Can you live a normal life? Yes, yes, yes!

The most important thing you need to do is not be in denial. This is easier said than done. Accepting you have lupus will help you move forward. You can be angry, scared, frustrated and sad—you might even try bargaining. They are all part of the grieving process. Yes, you will grieve—for the loss of who you were before lupus, for how you feel now, for what you can no longer do and for who you wanted to be.

In order to find happiness you need to work through those emotions and realize that they may be ever-changing. You can be angry in the morning, sad by noon and scared by night. Running from these emotions will not help. It will only create greater stress for you and we already know that stress and lupus do not mix well.

In the beginning there are a lot of things you must come to grips with—lupus, overlaying diseases, medication side effects, insurance coverage, family, work, dreams and much more. So take it one step at a time. Here are some ideas for you to think about even if you've had lupus for a long time—a fresh look at some of the issues facing patients today.

Reinvent yourself. Basically this means redefine who you are as a person. You are more than someone with lupus. Figure out what drives you, who are you at your inner core, and think of something that you would like to do. Create a list of many different ideas so that you are not limited in finding what will work for you. Don't let a disease or job define you. *Everyone* has something special that makes them unique.

Exercise. Yes, you are exhausted, busy and in pain, but you need to find some form of physical activity to do. Why? Because it will increase your endorphins, which in turn reduces your pain and gives you more energy. This might mean doing exercises in a chair, walking to the mailbox to get your mail instead of driving by, swimming, yoga, pilates or walking at a mall. These are just a few ideas to help your imagination. It is equally important to continue with a routine that you can realistically keep. So be reasonable and you will find in time some improvement.

Rest. This means listen to your body. It lets you know when it has had too much. And for those who feel you can just keep going, you can, but it *will* catch up with you. Try to avoid the crash-and-burn cycle. If you have a busy week at work, then limit your activities after work. When you have kids, set priorities and determine what can be done and what you may need help with. Family members or friends might be able to help with the picking up and dropping off. Resting also means getting enough sleep. There is nothing wrong with saying you need a good night's sleep in order to be fresh the next day. For some this may mean eight hours a night, others twelve. Everyone is different.

Nutrition. No, there isn't a diet specific for lupus patients, but everyone should eat healthy. Just because you have lupus does not mean that you should forget about eating right. Some foods will no longer agree with you, so try new things. You might also find that your gums are sorer due to certain medications so be sure to keep up with your dental hygiene as well.

Medical devices and gadgets. These will be your new best friends. Be sure to have a medic alert bracelet or necklace. That is essential to have in the event you need medical attention but are not able to provide information to paramedics. Don't be afraid to ask for medical devices or to use them—especially when it comes to assisting you walk or pick up things. It is also okay to ask your doctor for a handicapped placard. Parking far away means you may use up all your energy just walking to the door.

Looking good on the outside begins on the inside. Taking care of yourself emotionally will help you look better on the outside. It really will. Remember to smile—even when everything seems bleak, find something good in your day. Start with something small and work your way up. Over time you will find your list grows.

What to wear. How do you find the right clothes when your weight goes up and down or may even be distributed differently? Begin by thinking monochromatic color schemes because they make you appear taller and therefore slimmer. The real key is fluid, loose lines to your clothing. Also, think about buying clothes with elastic instead of zippers. It will be easier to pull on and off, plus will be more forgiving when your size fluctuates.

How do you fit shopping in when you have little energy or time? Fortunately, you can find most large chains offer their lines on the Internet—some even offer free shipping, so watch for specials. Even though you may not look the way you used to, you still should keep up your appearance. Letting yourself go will only make things worse. You won't feel good about yourself. You'd be surprised how the simplest things can make a difference. And don't forget that sunscreen and/or sun-protective clothing are the most important part of your wardrobe.

Hair and make-up. For most this is a very sensitive area. Hair loss, unwanted hair growth, rashes, and paler skin can make you not feel good about how you look. It is important to try and work with what you have, instead of just giving up. Rogaine has been known to help re-grow hair; waxing and bleaching can help with unwanted hair growth; concealers and cover-ups will help with reducing redness; and bronzers will give you a nice color. It will take time to find what will work best for you. Don't be discouraged if you try something and nothing happens—there are so many new products on the market that you *will* find what works for you.

Pamper yourself. Try using candles, aromatherapy and/or moisturizers, taking a bath, reading a book, going to a spa, buying yourself flowers just because or just taking a day about making you feeling better. Lupus is a complex disease. Not just medically, but physically and emotionally. Don't forget to give back to yourself. Sometimes we spend so much time taking care of others that we forget about ourselves.

Laughter is the best medicine. It truly helps. One of the toughest things to do for someone with any chronic illness is to get out of themselves and think about anything else. Watching a funny show or movie, reading a book, talking with friends or even reminiscing can help you feel good for those moments. You need to have some levity, even in the darkest times.

Good deeds. Don't isolate. This will keep you down. One of the easiest ways to get out of yourself is to do something nice for someone else, whether that means calling a friend who needs to talk, reading to kids or seniors, volunteering or making something special for someone. Helping others will actually make *you* feel a whole lot better.

Think ahead. Advance planning will help preserve your energy for when you need it most. It is a lot easier to do than it sounds. Instead of making two trips to a store, try and do it all at once—ask for a wheelchair or scooter if walking takes too much out of you and ask for help. One of hardest things to do can be asking for help. Planning will help you see what you have in front of you and may point out that you need to cut back if it becomes too much.

Doctor-patient relationship. Find the right doctor for you. Be sure they specialize in lupus. Don't be afraid or intimidated. Ask questions. It helps if you write a list out ahead of time so you are prepared. Keep a diary so you won't forget how you have been feeling. And most of all, be completely honest with your doctor. That is the only way they can give you the best care possible. This is especially true if you decide to no longer take your medication or to try herbal remedies. Fooling them is only going to harm you in the long run.

And lastly, *dream*. Never stop dreaming. You need to set goals, even if they are not what you originally started out with. Always strive for something, whether that means reading a book or taking a class. Lupus doesn't mean you can no longer accomplish anything. Success will come in new forms, and some may even be greater than you expected. Don't forget to love and to let others love you.

Hope is the thing
That perches in
And sings the
Without
And never

with feathers

the soul.

tune

the words,

stops at all.

—EMILY DICKINSON

GLOSSARY
of SYMPTOMS AND CONDITIONS

ALOPECIA: Hair loss can happen for many reasons, especially if you are taking certain medications such as steroids or chemotherapy. Sometimes, hair loss (random or patches) can happen at the onset of lupus. Depending upon the scarring, it may or may not grow back. The new hair that does grow in may be a different color or texture.

ANEMIA: We generally think of anemia as a vitamin deficiency that requires more meat and milk and iron pills. Lupus patients seem to have a variety of anemias based on low red blood cell counts, which your doctor can identify through monthly blood tests. You may require B-12 shots, high doses of steroids, chemotherapy drugs or blood transfusions, depending on the particular type of anemia, which can range from hemolytic to pernicious.

ANGIO-EDEMA: Edema, in general, means fluid retention, which can put stress on your heart and other organs, but angio-edema is a type that only puffs up your face, hands and feet. It will come and go at will, but can be helped by a variety of prescription drugs and a salt-free diet.

ANTIPHOSPHOLIPID SYNDROME: Also referred to as APS, sticky blood syndrome and Hughes' syndrome, it is a disorder that is often associated with autoimmune diseases and usually characterized by recurrent venous or arterial thrombosis. That means you may have abnormal clotting, often in the calves or lungs, which can result in strokes or heart attacks. The syndrome is usually controlled with anti-clotting drugs, including aspirin. Women with APS in childbearing years need to be aware of potential risks during pregnancy. Be sure to let your OB/GYN know.

ARTHRITIS: One of the most common complaints of lupus patients, arthritis is the inflammation of joints. But, unlike rheumatoid arthritis, it doesn't visibly disfigure your joints. To reduce inflammation, you may be prescribed non-steroidal anti-inflammatories (NSAIDs) and corticosteroids, sometimes in conjunction with other drugs, such as chemotherapy (also called immunosuppressive) drugs, which allow you to take lower doses of corticosteroids. Anti-malarial drugs also can help reduce the inflammation and pain of lupus arthritis.

ARTERIOSCLEROSIS: A condition that is marked by the loss of elasticity, thickening and hardening of the arteries. It can affect the brain, heart and walls of arteries and capillaries and is often seen in chronic nephritis (inflammation of the kidneys). It is associated with many health conditions.

AVASCULAR NECROSIS: This is another steroid-induced risk and is the death of a bone due to lack of circulation in that area, usually the hips. A surgeon will treat it by removing the dead part of the bone, but sometimes, if it is part of a joint, the entire joint will be removed and replaced with an artificial one.

BUTTERFLY (OR MALAR) RASH: This is the classic lupus rash. ("Malar" means "above the cheek bones") that goes over the bridge of your nose, as if a butterfly landed on your face. You may never get it or you may get one often. It's associated with a lupus flare and/or too much sun exposure, which you should definitely avoid.

CALCINOSIS: Calcium deposits that find their way to the surface of your skin, usually found on hands, forearms, nose and knees. It doesn't mean you drink too much milk or take too many calcium supplements, but it can be linked to infections and SLE, as well as other autoimmune diseases such as scleroderma.

CATARACTS: This visual problem that causes a carmelization of the lens is often caused by long-term use of steroids. When you have trouble reading street signs at night because there's a fog around them and feel like your glasses need to be continually cleaned, it may be time to see an ophthalmologist. Once diagnosed, your cataracts will be routinely checked. If needed, the cataract will be surgically removed and replaced with a new, artificial lens (not to be confused with contact lenses). Long-term use of anti-malarial drugs also causes eye problems that require frequent monitoring.

CREST SYNDROME: This is an acronym for five conditions: Calcinocis, which is calcium deposits rising to surface of the skin; Raynaud's phenomenon, a vascular problem that causes hands and feet to turn red, white and blue; Esophageal dysmotility, which refers to esophageal and intestinal problems; Sclerodactyly, a thickening and tightening of the skin that usually begins at the fingers; and Telangiectgasia, a general redness of the skin often seen on the face, upper torso and hands. The syndrome is associated with autoimmune diseases, such as lupus, scleroderma and polymyositis, and requires at least two of the five symptoms for diagnosis. Once diagnosed, new drugs may be added to your treatment plan and more tests may be ordered to keep the CREST syndrome under control.

CUSHING'S SYNDROME: Named for the doctor who discovered it, Cushing's syndrome includes swelling of the head, neck, shoulders and back and the possibility of glaucoma and cataracts. Most patients on steroids will get a thicker waistline, and, at its worst, the patient may develop a moon-shaped face, thick neck, hump on the back and a linebacker's torso. It's usually associated with higher doses of steroids, but some people can be affected at relatively low doses in a very short time. As you taper off steroids, the effects diminish and eventually some will disappear.

CELIAC SPRUE: An immune reaction to gluten (such as wheat). Celiac Sprue is a genetic, inheritable disease that damages the hair-like villi in the small intestine and causes malabsorption problems, including acute diarrhea, swollen belly, gas, edema and mouth sores. It is related to lupus and other autoimmune diseases and diagnosed with stool samples, biopsies of the small intestine and/or blood antibody tests. The good news is that a gluten-free diet helps stabilize the symptoms.

DEPRESSION: Doctors are still confused about depression in lupus patients. They are not sure if patients get depressed because of the chronic pain when you have lupus or if it is actually a symptom. Anti-depressants are now prescribed for depression and chronic pain. It has been found that by increasing your serotonin uptake, pain can be reduced, sleep patterns can be improved and depression can be alleviated. In some cases, increasing physical activity may also increase serotonin levels.

DISCOID LUPUS: A chronic cutaneous form of lupus that does not affect other organs. This skin disease affects the face, scalp, ears and arms, causing scarring and a change in the skin's pigment (scars may turn white). Discoid lupus can cause permanent hair loss in patches.

DISCOID SKIN LESIONS: Thick (or raised) and scaly skin lesions that can occur most commonly on sun-exposed parts of the body. They can be red or brown and rarely itch. When they heal they can leave a hypopigmented or whitish area behind. And even if you have SLE (not discoid lupus erythematosus), you can have discoid lesions.

DRUG-INDUCED LUPUS: The first thing rheumatologists look to rule out after a patient tests positive for lupus is whether or not the symptoms were brought on by other medications. Doctors have learned that various drugs—such as Apresoline (hydralazine), used to treat high blood pressure, INH (isoniazid), used to treat tuberculosis, Pronestyl (procainamide), used to treat heart arrhythmias, and even simple ibuprofen—are often the culprits. Some anti-depressants, penicillin and sulfa drugs also will mimic lupus. Symptoms are similar to early stages of SLE, with joint and muscle aches, fever, fatigue and sometimes inflammation of the heart.

LIBMAN-SACKS ENDOCARDITIS: Inflammation of the inner lining of the heart. The condition was discovered in 1923 by two physicians, Emanuel Libman and Benjamin Sacks. They learned that not only did these patients have heart murmurs but also evidence of antiphospholipid antibodies in their blood. Endocarditis can become a serious or even life-threatening infection. Therefore, before you have any surgical and/or dental procedures, be sure to consult your physician about taking antibiotics as a preventive measure.

FIBROMYALGIA: It's a condition, not a disease, that often has similar aches and pains associated with lupus. Also called fibrositis, it is not fatal but makes a person very sensitive to pain, as well as lack stamina. A rheumatologist can determine if you have fibromyalgia or lupus or both and begin treating you.

GASTROINTESTINAL LUPUS: Since the gastrointestinal tract is the largest organ system in our body, there are numerous conditions. Sore throats, oral lesions, difficulty swallowing and esophageal problems, such as acid reflux with heartburn, nausea and vomiting, are among the many signs that lupus may have invaded your upper gastrointestinal area. Conditions such as gastritis, hiatal hernias and gastric and peptic ulcers can occur, but diarrhea is most common. Diarrhea can be associated with lupus, side effects of drugs and/or bacterial infections that require antibiotics. Drugs to heal or protect you from ulcers include Priolsec, Aciphex, Tagamet, Zantac, Pepcid and Axid. Less likely conditions of the GI tract include ulcerative colitis, which is an inflammation requiring antibiotics or immunosuppressants, ascites (fluid in the belly) and malabsorption problems such as protein-losing enteropathy, which requires steroid treatment, and a seri-

ous type of cramping with bloody stools, which requires immediate attention to rule out an inflammation of the blood to the intestines or a perforated intestine. The pancreas is one of the last stops in the GI tract and when it becomes inflamed due to alcohol, diet, lupus or lupus drugs, it is called pancreatitis. Steroids are typically used to treat it, yet they must be withdrawn when there's a flare. As part of your monthly blood tests, your doctor will look for elevated enzymes called amylase and lipase to determine your progress. X-rays, scans and colonoscopy tests also can help diagnose or rule out many types of gastrointestinal conditions.

HASHIMOTO'S THYROIDITIS: Lupus patients are somewhat prone to thyroid problems, which can affect metabolism and energy levels. Hashimoto's thyroiditis (the opposite of Grave's disease) can cause palpitations, anxiety and elevated thyroid function tests. Endocrinologists will make the diagnosis and prescribe thyroid replacement pills.

IBS: This means irritable bowel syndrome and severe symptoms could prevent you from traveling, eating out, etc. Lupus and the medicines you take for it (NSAIDs, corticosteroids and chemotherapy) can affect your gastrointestinal tract with gas, nausea, vomiting, diarrhea and constipation that come and go in waves and may make you think you've got food poisoning or intestinal parasites. If you have a severe episode of IBS, see your doctor to rule out other conditions such as ulcerative colitis. For chronic IBS, drink plenty of fluids (water or sports drinks) and try to avoid spicy foods. During a flare, stick with eating easily digestible food (chicken broth, Jell-O, bananas, tea and toast) until you are feeling stable again. Antacids and acid-blocking drugs to avoid ulcers also may be prescribed.

JACCOUD'S ARTHROPATHY: This little-talked-about condition is named for the French physician Sigismond Jaccoud and refers to a chronic postrheumatic arthritis of the hands and feet that deforms joints while causing pain and loss of mobility. Jaccoud's Arthropathy (also referred to as a syndrome or disease) results from the inflammation and shortening of tendons and is sometimes linked to rheumatoid arthritis, lupus, rheumatic fever and scleroderma.

LEUKOPENIA: Too many white cells in your blood may mean an infection, but when you consistently have a low white blood cell count, you've got leukopenia. It's a rather common occurrence among lupus patients and usually has no symptoms, but your doctor will note it on routine blood tests. It's important to monitor because it may indicate you are about to have a flare.

LIVER PROBLEMS: Uncommonly, lupus will involve inflammation of the liver, which is the body's filtering system. Sometimes, all the strong drugs you take for lupus cause liver function to slow down, but your doctor will notice any problems on your routine blood tests before it becomes a serious problem. Usually, your doctor will prescribe corticosteroids or other immunosuppressants to treat it.

LUPUS CYSTITIS: Lupus doesn't often manifest itself by inflaming the lining of the bladder (noted by pain upon urination and blood in urine) but it can happen. The good news is that a urologist can usually diagnose it by a procedure called cystoscopy. It can be treated with drugs or by a medical procedure that stretches the bladder and minimizes the chance of infection or inflammation. And because lupus medications, particularly steroids, can make a woman's bladder lining and vaginal walls thin, estrogen creams can be prescribed to minimize the discomfort.

LUPUS NEPHRITIS: This is lupus in the kidneys, usually detected through blood and urine tests that indicate blood urea nitrogen and/or creatine. It's often referred to as "spilling protein" into the blood. It is one of the more serious conditions of lupus and therefore is constantly watched by your physician. If blood tests are elevated, you may be referred to a nephrologist, or kidney specialist, in addition to your rheumatologist and will be put on a course of action that may include drugs, such as steroids and chemotherapy, as well as changes in your diet. Kidney involvement in lupus is not usually felt in the kidney area, but rather noted by swollen ankles and abdomen and a generally bloated feeling. There are varying degrees of the disease, ranging from a drug-induced nephritis, which requires your doctor to cut back on certain medications (remember that many good drugs have bad side effects), to renal inflammation and kidney failure, which can require dialysis and transplantation. But before that, doctors will rule out other diseases and study a biopsy of your kidney tissue.

LUPUS PANNICULITIS: It's also called lupus profundus, and it is a chronic condition that primarily affects subcutaneous fat and results in painful lesions that often scar, atrophy and cause disfigurement. The lesions are usually found on the trunk of the body, breasts, buttocks and face. Your doctor can confirm it with skin and blood tests and treat it with antimalarial drugs, steroids and/or immunosuppressants such as Imuran.

MIXED CONNECTIVE TISSUE DISEASE (MCTD): This disease is as its name states—it is a mixture of connective tissue diseases. It can also be referred to as Undifferentiated Connective Tissue Disease. Basically, a patient will exhibit symptoms that are from more than one autoimmune disease, most often from rheumatoid arthritis, lupus, scleroderma and polymyositis. Patients will also test positive for anti-RNP antibodies. Until a single disease manifests itself and you continue to present a variety of connective tissues disease symptoms, doctors will continue to treat you as having MCTD. The severity of symptoms can range; however, typically you will be spared any organ involvement with MCTD.

MOUTH SORES: A very common manifestation of lupus, mouth sores (also called lesions and ulcers) are usually small craters that occur inside the cheeks or on the tongue, roof of the mouth or gums. Many are painless, but others are not. Sometimes mouth sores look like large blood blisters and will not only hurt, but bleed. For those that are painful, your doctor can prescribe a dental paste such as triamcinolone (Kenalog in Orabase). Gargling with a mixture of warm water and salt also can help.

MYOCARDITIS: A cardiac disorder that may mimic a heart attack with chest pain and a rapid pulse. This can happen due to the inflammation of the heart muscle. In more severe cases the heart muscle can be permanently damaged. This will require close monitoring. The diagnosis is usually made by catheterization and/or biopsy of the myocardium (heart muscle). Medical treatment includes anti-inflammatories, most often corticosteriods.

NASAL ULCERS: A common symptom that may or may not cause nose bleeds or infections. Your doctor will routinely check your nasal passages for crater-like lesions (similar to mouth sores) that indicate lupus activity, as well as holes in the cartilage (called a perforated septum). You can get relief with petroleum jelly and prescription ointments such as Bactroban, but once you get these sores, they tend to make repeat performances.

NEONATAL LUPUS: This type of lupus affects newborn babies whose mothers may or may not have lupus but who carry certain antibodies that can cross the placenta and damage the fetus. They are maternal anti-Ro (anti-SSA) antibodies and they can cause a transient rash or permanent damage to the conduction system of the infant's heart, causing heart blockage.

NEUROPSYCHIATRIC SLE: A condition in which lupus has invaded the nervous system, which is noted by a huge variety of symptoms that can range from severe headaches and vision problems (swelling of the optic nerve) to tremors and balance problems, seizures, strokes and possible psychosis. More often, lupus patients have trouble with depression and cognitive dysfunction (which creates trouble with memory, numbers or concentration). It may come and go or become permanent. If you have any concerns, discuss them with your doctor so that proper testing and evaluations are conducted. Sometimes, side effects from medications can be the cause of neuropsychiatric SLE. Peripheral nervous system conditions can include damage to the motor nerves that causes numbness and "pins-and-needles" sensations in hands, feet and the face, which can sometimes be relieved with steroids, other anti-inflammatory drugs, splints and, in more severe cases, surgery to decompress the nerves. When lupus affects the central nervous system, the spinal cord and brain can be involved.

This is the most serious form of nervous system problem that can include inflammation of the brain, which can cause psychotic behavior and hallucinations. It is treated with high doses of steroids administered intravenously or by pulse dosing and possible use of antipsychotic preparations such as Thorazine, Haldol and Stelazine. If you have continuous headaches or any of these symptoms, your doctor will order a complete neurological workup that may include an MRI of the brain to look for lesions or evidence of strokes, tumors or atrophy. Other tests include nerve conduction tests called electroencephalograms (EEGs) and electromyograms (EMGs), a spinal tap (injection in the lower back) for examination of the spinal fluid, and neuropsychological tests. Once a diagnosis is made, your doctor will work with you to find the correct drugs and dosage to help control your condition.

NEUTROPENIA: A lack of the bacteria-killing white cells (called neutrophils) in circulating blood, often due to active lupus, viral infections or chemotherapy. With a shortage of these white cells, your body is vulnerable to attack from numerous infections; however, it is extremely rare.

OCULAR MANIFESTATIONS (RETINAL VASCULITIS, OPTIC NEURITIS, SCLERITIS): Lupus can result in inflammation of various parts of the eye that can result in visual damage. Involvement of blood vessels in the back of the eye can result in retinal vasculitis; involvement of the nerve connecting the eye to the brain can result in optic neuritis; and involvement of the outside layer of the eye itself can result in scleritis, an inflammation of the white membrane covering the eyeball. Your doctor will order an ophthalmology consultation for any of these situations for proper treatment.

OSTEOARTHRITIS: A type of degenerative arthritis that is commonly found among lupus patients. It's often in the fingers, where the cartilage deteriorates and bone rubs on bone, which makes it painful to pick up things, type or play musical instruments. But it also can affect your neck, spine, knees and hips. Your doctor can diagnose it through X-rays and order custom-made plastic splints for your hands to help minimize pain and increase motion range. There's no cure and steroids won't relieve the pain, but hot showers and baths give some relief.

OSTEOPOROSIS: A bone-weakening disease often associated with women past menopause. It can cause painful fractures and a curvature of the upper back. Unfortunately, lupus patients on high and/or long-term doses of steroids are at greater risk. Your doctor will monitor you often with bone density tests and possibly full body scans. Treatments include calcium pills and medications such as Fosamax or Actonel to strengthen your bones.

OVERLAP FEATURES: Sometimes lupus can include features from other less common "crossover-cousins," such as polymyositis with muscle inflammation; scleroderma, which involves tightening of the skin; and vasculitis, which is an inflammation of blood vessels that can range from little red dots on your skin to strokes and heart attacks. Your doctor will determine these features, based on your symptoms and blood tests, and prescribe treatment.

PERICARDITIS: A cardiac disorder, which causes inflammation of the pericardium (sac of the heart) and is noted for pain in the chest that sometimes can be relieved by bending forward. Your doctor may use an X-ray, echocardiogram (heart ultrasound) or simply a stethoscope to diagnose it. Sometimes there is fluid (called effusion) in the pericardium that requires removal or steroid treatment, but this disorder is not usually organ-threatening.

PHOTOSENSITIVITY: An acute sensitivity to sunlight and ultraviolet light found in most offices. Too much of it can cause your skin to feel like it is on fire and sometimes creates a redness, rash or blisters, often on the face and chest. Unfortunately, it's more than a sunburn situation, as it can cause a lupus flare with symptoms of fatigue and fever. To avoid it, wear sunscreen and protective clothing, while limiting your time in the sun. Photosensitivity (also called sun sensitivity rash) is common with lupus and can also be exacerbated by many medications.

PLEURITIS: The main symptom of pleuritis is pleurisy (chest pain) when taking a deep breath. It is caused by the inflammation of the thin membrane sac that envelops the lung and it occurs in nearly fifty percent of lupus patients. If fluid forms in your lung, you can get pleural *effusion*. Your doctor can detect effusions by chest X-rays, ultrasounds or CT (computer tomography) scans and determine a course of treatment that may include anti-inflammatory drugs or antibiotics.

POLYMYOSITIS: A chronic inflammatory disease of the muscles, causing muscle weakness that can be improved by many of the same drugs, such as steroids and immunosuppressants, that already are prescribed for lupus. Physical therapy is important to strengthen muscles and increase range of motion.

PULMONARY HYPERTENSION: Think of this as high blood pressure of the lung arteries. It can vary in its severity, and it most often begins with difficulty breathing. Your doctor may recommend a consultation with a pulmonary specialist.

RAYNAUD'S PHENOMENON: This is a vascular spasm that causes your hands and feet to turn red, white and blue when you are cold or stressed. Generally, just keeping warm with socks or mittens will help, but severe cases can be treated with calcium-blocking drugs and topical nitroglycerin. It generally remains mild, but left untreated it can cause lesions that could result in gangrene, especially of the tips of toes and fingers.

SCLERODERMA: A first cousin of lupus, scleroderma is an autoimmune disease in which the skin gradually loses its elasticity and hardens (called sclerosis). The skin thickens and scars on the outside of the body, primarily on the upper torso and thighs, and can result in deformities. But the more serious symptoms are the hardening of the tissues on the inside of the intestines, bowel wall and blood vessels.

SJOGREN'S SYNDROME: An autoimmune disorder noted for dry eyes, dry mouth and arthritis. Some of the more common symptoms are "gritty-feeling" eyes, a decrease in tear production, vaginal dryness and difficulty swallowing food. If you experience any of these symptoms, alert your doctor. There are medications available to minimize your discomfort.

TREMORS: Although often associated with other autoimmune diseases such as Parkinson's disease or muscular dystrophy, tremors of the hands and legs are seen in some lupus patients. Nerve conduction tests can determine their source. Although this can be scary, your doctor will be able to prescribe medication to eliminate or reduce these tremors.

THROMBOCYTOPENIA: This condition means a low platelet count. It is usually noted on a blood test, long before you get any actual symptoms. When it gets severe, such as a platelet count of less than ten thousand, it can result in spontaneous internal bleeding. Most patients with this manifestation respond to medication.

VASCULITIS: This refers to the inflammation of the blood vessels caused by inflammation of the blood vessel walls from an immune reaction, such as lupus. It can be as serious as blood clots that cause heart attacks and strokes, but it is most often seen on the skin of lupus patients as tiny red dots called petechiae, a fishnet pattern called livedo reticularis or raised black-and-blue areas called purpura. Once noted, your doctor will consider more aggressive lupus treatment, such as steroids. Vasculitis can also thin the skin and cause easy bruising (bleeding under the skin), so it is important to make your doctor aware of any new bruises or lesions.

*I think a hero is
an ordinary individual
who finds strength
to persevere and endure
despite overwhelming
obstacles.*

—Christopher Reeve

CHAPTER 3

MIX IT UP

Hope is the better side of courage.

—HONORÉ DE BALZAC

Most people think that once you know what is causing their symptoms, then they can simply take a pill and feel better. That's not true for most lupus patients.

In fact, lupus is one of a few diseases that do not have a medication specifically designed to treat it. All of the medications used to treat lupus are borrowed from other diseases and medical conditions, including cancer, edema, organ transplants and so on.

As a patient, you must learn to cope with having this disease, deal with the medication side effects and make lifestyle changes. It's one thing to come to terms with having a disease without a cure, but the drug side effects can sometimes be worse than lupus. Many times you find yourself taking additional drugs to counteract the side effects.

This disease is challenging for physicians to treat. Not only is there no single cure-all drug, but the illness can manifest itself in myriad ways.

There is an expression that, like snowflakes, no two lupus patients are alike. It's true.

While there may be similar symptoms, each person responds differently to treatments. Patient A may go into remission by taking Plaquenil, while Patient B may be allergic to almost everything and Patient C may continue to decline. Rheumatologists must use a combination of drugs that collectively will reduce disease activity.

You may have heard this combination of drugs referred to as a *cocktail*. This sounds a lot more hip than a pill regimen or prescription list and hopefully makes it easier to swallow. Ingredients will vary, depending on your particular lupus conditions. Once you've received your cocktail recipe, ask questions. Be sure you understand how and when to take the drugs, what side effects to expect and what alternatives are available if you feel you cannot tolerate a specific drug.

The key to survival is more than medications. It requires inner strength and new approaches to your everyday life. This may be one of the hardest areas you will have to cope with—especially when your physical appearance changes and you are limited to minimal sun exposure. And traditional cocktails may no longer be allowed. For most patients, the use of alcohol is not encouraged.

Now that you have a lupus diagnosis, here's a sampling of what your doctors may order for that medical cocktail.

MEDICATIONS

ANTI-DEPRESSANTS: Whether it's the disease or simply dealing with the disease, you may become depressed and anxious and have trouble sleeping. There are several medications that can help. Among them are tricylic antidepressants, such as Flexeril, Sinequan, Elavil and Pamelor, which not only help depression but relax muscles. Others include benzodiazeprines such as Valium, Klonopin, Xanax and Librium, but these are potentially addictive. Serotonin reuptake inhibitors such as Prozac, Zoloft, Effexor and Paxil can be helpful used alone or with tricyclics, which can create a better sense of well-being to deal with your disease. Follow instructions carefully. Many of them suggest not drinking, driving or taking with certain other drugs. These drugs are usually taken at bedtime. It is important to be open with your doctor about your questions and/or concerns and to maintain good communication with him/her.

ANTIHISTAMINES: Lupus patients seem to be more inclined to allergies, whether they're drugs, pets, food or plants. A small percentage of patients experience hives. Drugs originally designed for allergy relief can also be helpful in getting rid of hives. These medications include antihistamines such as Allegra, Singulair, Zyrtec and Benadryl, as well as other non-antihistamines such as nasal sprays, decongestants and steroids. Allergy shots are usually not advised for lupus patients. Not all of these medications will make you sleepy.

ANTIMALARIAL DRUGS: During World War II, many of the three million Americans in the South Pacific were given antimalarial drugs. Military doctors had discovered that not only did the drugs help malaria but also rheumatoid or lupus-related diseases because of their anti-inflammatory properties and the ability to turn off certain autoimmune pathways. Today, hydroxycholorquine is a front-line defense for many lupus patients, prescribed as HCQ or Plaquenil. It is the only antimalarial approved by the FDA for use in SLE and is effective in about eighty percent of patients with non-organ threatening disease. It not only helps fatigue, aches, rashes and sun sensitivity, but also improves Sjogren's Syndrome and lowers cholesterol while inhibiting platelets. Unfortunately, some patients cannot tolerate this quinine-based drug, and others suffer retina problems. Occasionally, other antimalarials drugs are used, such as Aralen for serious lupus rashes, and quinacrine or Atabrine for fatigue and cognitive impairment. Your doctor will request ophthalmologist exams at least once a year to avoid visual problems and also will order regular lab tests to monitor your progress.

ANTI-SEIZURE DRUGS: Seizures can occur with lupus, and doctors routinely prescribe drugs to avoid or minimize the possibilities. Among them are Neurontin and Gabritril, which are anticonvulsants; they also help relieve nerve pain, headaches and tremors. Most patients take these drugs at bedtime.

ARTIFICIAL TEARS: Lupus patients suffering from Sjogren's Syndrome and the dry, gritty-feeling in their eyes can get relief from over-the-counter products that provide artificial tears, such as Alcon's Tears Naturale Forte, which comes in a bottle. Be sure to drink plenty of water, avoid contact lenses and smoke-filled rooms and try hypoallergenic eye makeup. Finally, try steamy showers and humidifiers to create a moister environment for dry eyes.

BLOOD PRESSURE MEDICATIONS: As lupus patients gain weight on steroids, they often retain salt and fluids that can cause blood pressure to rise. To avoid heart attacks and strokes (as well as irritability and mental confusion), doctors often prescribe drugs that help lower blood pressure, such as benazepril (Lotensin), which is an angiotensin-coverting enzyme (ACE) inhibitor. Other medications for high blood pressure include beta-adrenergic blocking agents such as Inderal, Atacand and Avapro. These drugs are usually taken at bedtime, as they can make you drowsy or dizzy. Your doctor may ask you to keep a daily record of your blood pressure to gauge improvement, but patients should also be walking when possible, eating smaller portions and cooking without salt.

CALCIUM CHANNEL BLOCKERS: Calcium channel blockers (also called calcium antagonists) are sometimes used to treat angina pectoris (chest pain that can mimic or precede a heart attack), hypertension and other heart problems because they slow down the heart rate and relax blood vessels. These relatively new drugs block passage of calcium into the heart muscle cells but not into the blood stream; they don't stop calcium from getting into the bloodstream and to help strengthen bones. Among the many brands are Procardia, Adalat, Cardizem, Dilacor, Calan, Verelan, Isoptin, Cardene, Norvasc, Plendil and DynaCirc. Like most meds that help, there are also side effects, which include easy bruising, diarrhea, nausea, dizziness and also kidney and liver problems. You will be closely monitored when prescribed these medications.

CORTICOSTEROIDS: Ever since their introduction in 1950, these anti-inflammatory drugs, usually referred to as steroids, have been the lupus lifesaver. If non-steroidal drugs have not helped, you'll most likely be prescribed a derivative of cortisone, such as Prednisone or medrol. Although they quickly can halt a major lupus flare, lupus lesions and joint inflammation, steroids are a double-edged sword. They do good things for you, but long-term use and/or high doses of steroids can cause your metabolism to slow down, add weight in unusual places, make your hair fall out (or grow in unusual places) and/or cause thinning of the bones, cataracts, glaucoma, ulcers, edema and mood changes. It's such a powerful drug that you cannot abruptly stop taking it; you should taper off under a doctor's supervision. Baseline bone density evaluations will be continually monitored in an effort to avoid osteoporosis and other bone-thinning problems. So, in addition to steroids, you may be prescribed bone-strengthening bisphosphonates, such as Actonel or Fosamax, plus calcium supplements with vitamin D. Steroids can be administered orally (Prednisone, methylprednisolone or Medrol, dexamethasone or decadron), by injection (kenalog or depomedrol) or intravenously (often called steroids with sulmedrol). All of the steroid preparations have essentially the same side effect profile except for few subtle differences. Side effects are predominantly determined by potency, dose and duration of use.

DHEA (DEHYDROEPIANDROSTERONE): A mild male hormone that scientists have discovered can help some lupus patients with osteoporosis and cognitive dysfunction, as well as provide an energy boost. Do not try this without consent from your doctor, as there are potentially severe side effects that could be harmful to you. It is also important to note that DHEA is not monitored or approved by the FDA.

DIURETICS: Prescription medicines used to eliminate through urination accumulation of body fluids due to edema, which often plagues steroid-dependent lupus patients. Lasix is a commonly used diuretic pill and is usually prescribed in tandem with a potassium supplement such as K-Dur.

IMMUNOSUPPRESSIVES: These drugs, also referred to as steroid-sparing agents, allow you to take fewer steroids while calming down your overactive immune systems. They can also relieve prominent inflammation of the joints, fatigue or cognitive dysfunction. They are chemotherapy drugs but not those typically used for cancer treatment. Lupus patients are often prescribed methotrexate, which is a rheumatoid arthritis drug, leflunomide (Arava) or azathioprine (Imuran). Less widely used drugs include retinoids (Accutane and Soriatene), antileprosy drugs (thalidomide, Lamprene and dapsone), topical immunophylles (Elidel and Protopic) or Salgen or Evoxac for those with Sjogren's Syndrome *and* lupus. In addition to DHEA, other hormonal drugs are used, such as danazol for low platelet counts or bromocriptine, which lowers prolactin levels in mild cases of lupus. Raynaud's phenomenon also can be helped with other drugs in this category, which include calcium channel blockers such as nifedipine and topical nitrogylcerine. For lupus patients with serious organ-threatening disease, doctors may use Cytoxan, leukeran or nitrogen mustard, which are the most toxic drugs in this category; each of which carries risks of sterility, infection or an increased risk of future cancer such as leukemia or lymphoma. Before you begin taking immunosuppressive medications, be sure you understand the side effects and the reason they are being prescribed. Keep a medical diary and call your doctor if a new condition arises—don't wait until the next appointment. Your doctor may lower your dose or add a drug to avoid symptoms such as nausea or diarrhea. In recent years, mycophenolate mofetil (cellcept) has become a popular alternative to treat relatively severe organ-threatening disease with a potentially less toxic side effect profile, in comparison to drugs such as cytoxan; however, cellcept does have some risk in terms of infections, blood count abnormalities and nausea. A new medication, rituximab, is now being used with some early success in lupus. This medication is an antibody against a marker on B lymphocytes, which are white cells involved in the lupus attack on the body. It is hoped that by stopping overactive B lymphocytes, the lupus process can be arrested. Early reports have been encouraging in terms of benefit without significant infectious side effects.

NON-STEROIDAL ANTI-INFLAMMATORY DRUGS: These are known as NSAIDs, and although none of them are approved by the Food and Drug Administration specifically for lupus, about seventy-five percent of patients use them to help with headaches, muscle aches, joint pain, fevers and pleuritic or pericardial symptoms—even reducing the size of swollen glands. These drugs include over-the-counter aspirin, ibuprofen and naproxen with brand names such as Advil or Aleve, as well as antagonists that are prescription drugs such as Feldene, Mobic, Lodine, Toradol, Relafen, Meclomen and Ponstel. Your doctor needs to know if you are taking over-the-counter meds before prescribing others.

PAIN MEDICATIONS: These drugs range from aspirin to morphine; however, one of the most commonly used is Vicodin. Since most of them are narcotics, you will be closely monitored by your doctor, but sometimes they are needed for post-surgery, broken bones and severe joint pain. If you are having trouble dealing with pain, talk to your doctor about the possibilities, so you can focus on getting well. For some types of pain, your doctor may give you an injection in a joint or suggest a lidocaine patch that you place over a sore joint for no more than twelve hours.

SALIVARY SUBSTITUTES OR STIMULANTS: When your throat is dry (the term is xerostomia) and your voice is hoarse due to Sjogren's Syndrome or lupus-induced synovitis I (inflamed vocal chords), there are a variety of aids that range from steroid aerosol sprays to chicken soup. Other ways to help dry mouth syndrome include mouthwashes for sore throats, hard candies, cough drops, water with lemon slices and room humidifiers. A drug called Humbid also can add moisture to the lungs and throat, while Pilocapine can increase tear production and promote salivary secretions.

TACROLIMIS CREAM: This is an immune-suppressing drug (such as Prograf and Protopic) originally created to help stop rejection of organ transplants. But like other immunosupressants, it has other uses. As an ointment it can relieve the pain and itching of skin diseases such as atopic dermatitis, psoriasis and discoid lupus. In most cases it is applied twice a day for one week.

An important reminder: Many of the drugs in your treatment plan have the same warning that alcoholic cocktails carry: Don't drink and drive. Also, don't count on your memory in case you're sick or in a car accident. Always carry a card or medical résumé with you to help an emergency physician or your own doctor (who may see dozens of patients a day). You also should have a list of medications and foods that cause allergic reactions (such as shellfish or sulfa drugs) for yourself, your doctors *and* your pharmacist.

A strong positive mental attitude

will create more miracles than any wonder drug.

—PATRICIA NEAL

MEDICAL TESTS

Of course, you knew there'd be a few tests, right?
But every month and so many types?
Here's a cheat sheet on what types of tests to expect with lupus, why you need them and what doctors are looking for.

BIOPSIES: A biopsy is the removal of living tissue for medical examination. It can be as simple as a needle injected into a body part, or it can require a hospital visit for the surgical removal of a larger piece of tissue. The procedure can hurt, but it is incredibly important for diagnosis of a disease or condition, and also can rule out something you might be fearing, such as cancer. Make your doctor explain it in great detail before the appointment, so you won't have any unpleasant surprises at the medical center.

BLOOD TESTS: After your doctor performs a physical examination and hopefully a personal interview with you, a complete blood count (CBC), including blood chemistries and various autoantibody tests, will be ordered along with a urine test. This will provide important information about you and your condition, and it's very critical for that first appointment with your lupus doctor. It will be compared to future blood tests to check progress or new conditions.

A CBC checks the count and types of white blood cells; red cells, hemoglobin and hematocrit (to check for anemia); and platelets. All three cell lines (white, red and platelets) may be affected by lupus. Additionally, your doctor may need to monitor these counts to be sure you are not having a side effect from medication used to treat the disease. A chemistry panel can check for electrolyte imbalance, elevated blood sugar (a possible side effect of steroid therapy) and liver or kidney abnormalities. Autoantibodies such as ANA (anti-nuclear antibodies), anti-doublestranded DNA, anti-SSA, SSB, anti-RNP, anti-Smith, as well as complement levels, can allow a physician to definitively make a diagnosis. Serial monitoring of the anti-doublestranded DNA and C3 and C4 complement levels can

help your doctor determine if the activity of the lupus disease is getting worse or is responding to the treatment.

Although giving blood isn't exactly pleasant, it's a necessity. If the sight of a needle frightens you, just focus on a picture on the wall—even a chart—and it will go quickly. Also ask for a pediatric-sized or butterfuly needle, both of which will be less painful. Be sure to ask for paper tape to be put over the cotton ball at the injection site, as lupus skin is quite sensitive to adhesive tapes. Your doctor will discuss the results of the tests with you during the following appointment. You should always ask for a copy of your test results for your own records.

BONE DENSITOMETRY SCAN: When prescribed steroids you will routinely have these scans performed to closely monitor your bone density. It may also be ordered if you are experiencing arthritic pain. This test is able to detect osteopenia, osteoporosis and hip and knee problems. It is painless; you simply lie on your back while the test is performed. On the day you have the test, you can eat and take your meds, but you shouldn't take calcium supplements for twenty-four hours prior to test time.

BONE SCAN: This test is done in a hospital and is a nuclear medicine procedure. You'll be asked to come into the hospital for an injection of an isotope and then come back about three hours later. During that time you need to drink several glasses of water to clear the kidneys of any isotopes not picked up by the bones; you are able to eat during this time. Then you'll empty your bladder and a technician will position you on a long scanning table that is somewhat like a

MRI table, except you're not left in a closed tube. The test takes about an hour and it allows the doctor to detect bone tumors or breaks, arthritis and other conditions. It's much more reliable and complete than X-rays. This same procedure can be used for the lungs, brain, kidneys and other organs.

COMPUTERIZED AXIAL TOMOGRAPHY (CAT) SCAN: This is similar to an X-ray but on a much higher level. A CAT scan, performed in the radiology department of a medical center, will scan your body to form a three-dimensional computer model of your insides, internally and externally. The reason your doctor might order this is because it allows him to see behind things that appear as shadows in a traditional X-ray. It is totally painless, quick and easy.

ELECTROMYOGRAMS (EMGS) AND NERVE CONDUCTION TEST (NCS): This electrical study is performed with nerve conduction velocity testing to determine any peripheral nerve problems you may have with lupus, ranging from carpal tunnel syndrome to muscle lesions. If you have had numbness or tingling in your arms or feet, this test may be ordered for you, and it's one of the tests that does involve some pain—or at least discomfort—as a doctor in the neurology department will hook you up to a monitor and insert very small needles into various muscles in your arm, leg, neck and back. The NCS part of the test is less painful and evaluates muscle and nerve damage by placing electrodes on your skin and sending electrical shocks that are picked up on a monitor. To prepare for the tests, be sure to scrub your skin well with a mild soap and avoid lotions, oils and bath powders before arriving. You may be told you can drive yourself home but you may be more exhausted and sore than other non-lupus patients, so arrange for a ride home.

ELECTROCARDIOGRAM (EKG): This painless test gives your doctor many clues to the health of your heart, as it provides heart rate and rhythm and the size of the heart chamber. If you have complained to your doctor of chest pain or have palpitations or an irregular heart beat, this test may be ordered for you.

ELECTROENCEPHALOGRAM (EEG): An electrical study of the central nervous system that helps map the brain and enables your doctor to see where a seizure might be coming from and why. It also determines if you have central nervous system lupus, which may be referred to as lupus psychosis or lupus cerebritis (inflammation of the brain).

MAGNETIC RESONANCE IMAGING (MRI): This is a test that involves lying on a long table inside of a tube, which might make you a little nervous, but it's one the best sources of information for a doctor. Be sure to let your doctor know if you are claustrophobic. Many hospitals now have larger tubes that reduce the possible claustrophobic feeling. It's better than an X-ray because it shows very clear pictures of everything, from joint damage to brain lesions to cancer. Newly diagnosed lupus patients may be given an MRI, which will serve as a comparison for future tests. Since the machine uses a large magnet, you'll need to leave your jewelry at home. But consider bringing socks to keep your feet warm, especially if you have Raynaud's phenomenon. Also, be sure to inform your doctor if you have a heart pacemaker, implanted pumps or metal parts or if you are pregnant, as these conditions may not make you a good candidate for an MRI.

ULTRASOUND: One of the simplest visualization procedures in the diagnosis of various lupus conditions, which works by bouncing sound waves off the organ. Also referred to as a sonogram, it's a painless procedure in which you lay on a table and a technician puts a jelly-like substance on various spots of your body and a little microphone attached to a machine is moved around to catch and record the sounds. Then the ultrasound technician will take still photographs of images on the screen and give them and a report to your doctor. Ultrasounds are one of the few tests in which there's a little interaction: You can actually see the motion on the monitor next to you.

URINE TESTS/CULTURES: A urinalysis is a laboratory examination of your urine. Technicians will check it for blood cells and bacteria that may indicate infection or kidney disease. When warranted, a culture may be ordered to see if any infection grows from the bacteria. Urine tests will become part of your monthly ritual.

X-RAYS: This staple of the medical profession was discovered by Wilhelm Roentgen in 1895 and earned him the Nobel Prize for physics. The procedure is quick and easy and usually requires you to wear a cotton "gown" and stand (or lay) in front of a machine while a film is put in it. Then the technician goes behind a wall and asks you to hold your breath, and, in the case of a chest X-ray, the machine photographs the outline of bones and shows shadows that indicate possible problems. If more information is needed, you may require a CAT scan or MRI. Be sure to let your doctor know if you are pregnant before having an X-ray.

Not knowing when the dawn will come, I open every door.

—EMILY DICKINSON

CHAPTER 4

KNOWLEDGE IS POWER

The more you learn about lupus, the more you can help your doctor help you.

So, where do you start?

The public library, bookstores, doctors' offices, the Internet and Lupus International. The following books are all available from Lupus International, by visiting www.lupusinternational.com or calling 888-532-2322.

BOOKS

The New Sjogren's Syndrome Handbook
By Steven Carsons, M.D. and Elaine K. Harris

Total Relaxation
By John R. Harvey, Ph.D.
Includes a CD with step-by-step relaxation techniques.

Lupus Q&A: Everything You Need to Know
By Robert G. Lahita M.D., Ph.D. and Robert H. Phillips, Ph.D.
This newly released book contains a wealth of information about lupus, related diseases, treatments and how to live with the complexities of having an autoimmune disease.

Women and Autoimmune Disease: The Mysterious Ways Your Body Betrays Itself
By Robert G. Lahita, M.D., and Ina Yalof.
Dr. Lahita, considered a world-class immunologist, rheumatologist and lupus expert, blends his warmth, compassion and extraordinary medical expertise, which comes from more than twenty years as a leading research scientist and caring physician.

All About Osteoarthritis: The Definitive Resource for Arthritis Patients and Their Families
By Nancy E. Lane, M.D. and Daniel J. Wallace, M.D.
Presents the most up-to-date and comprehensive information on osteoarthritis.

Coping with Lupus: A Practical Guide to Alleviating the Challenges of Systemic Lupus Erythematosus
By Robert H. Phillips, Ph.D.
Creative coping strategies for the frustrating symptoms of this autoimmune disease.

Beyond Chaos: One Man's Journey Alongside His Chronically Ill Wife
By Gregg Piburn
Working together to survive the emotional, mental and physical challenges of chronic illness.

The Sjogren's Syndrome Survival Guide
By Teri P. Rumpf, Ph.D, and Katherine Morland Hammitt
Good practical advice and self-help strategies for coping with Sjogren's Syndrome.

Disability Workbook: For Social Security Applicants
By Douglas M. Smith
How to prove your claim for disability insurance benefits.

All About Fibromyalgia: A Guide for Patients and Their Families
By Daniel J. Wallace, M.D. and Janice Brock Wallace

Fibromyalgia: An Essential Guide for Patients and Their Families
By Daniel J. Wallace, M.D. and Janice Brock Wallace.
A comprehensive guide from exercise to medications.

The Lupus Book: A Guide for Patients and Their Families
By Daniel J. Wallace, M.D.
Excellent and easy to understand for lupus patients and their friends and family members. This book has been a staple for several years.

ABOUT LUPUS INTERNATIONAL

Lupus International is a non-profit organization founded in 1983. According to organizational by-laws, Lupus International's mission is to provide patient education, to encourage moral support and understanding for all forms of lupus, to promote public education about lupus and the exchange of knowledge about lupus, to cooperate with health professionals to improve the standards of diagnosis, care, services and treatment of those suffering from lupus, to represent those who have lupus, their families, friends and associates and serve as their foundation spokesperson, to encourage the creation of state and local organizations dedicated to serving those who have lupus and their families, to cooperate and assist with such organizations, to provide services that will benefit and improve the health and welfare of lupus sufferers, to encourage research to discover the causes and improve the methods of treating, diagnosing, curing and preventing lupus and discoid lupus.

Lupus International is as close as a toll-free phone call to (888) 532-2322 or a visit to www.lupusinternational.com. Here, you'll receive instant help, including the latest news about lupus research, articles that give tips on how to live with lupus, the location of the nearest support group and membership information. You'll be able to chat with others on our online chat room and "ask the doctor" in a question-and-answer format, accessing doctors who are members of the Lupus International Medical Board.

Members also receive LupusLine, a quarterly magazine packed with information on the latest news in lupus research, which offers helpful articles on daily living. This is a great magazine to take along on a car ride, to read in a waiting room or to provide to a friend or family member struggling to understand.

Utilizing books, pamphlets and Lupus International's robust Website will help you begin your education. When you're worried about a new symptom or want to get a better understanding of your particular diagnosis, you can access your home library. You'll feel like a team leader, rather than a victim.

EPILOGUE

During my career as a journalist I have had the pleasure of interviewing numerous celebrities, often in their home. Among them are athletes Shaquille O'Neil and Mike Piazza; comedians Phyllis Diller, Doris Roberts and the late Rodney Dangerfield; Hollywood icon Frankie Avalon, and young stars such as Kirsten Dunst. Plus world-class fashion designers, including Donna Karan, Tommy Hilfiger, Max Azria of BCBG, Valentino and the late Bill Blass.

None bared their souls like the people in this book.

The lupus patients who opened their hearts and homes to me over the past year are a true representation of the myriad people this incurable disease strikes: Rich, poor and middle-class; African-American, Caucasian, Hispanic and Asian; teens to senior citizens. And a few men, although it is primarily a woman's disease. Some of them will die before old age; others will lead relatively stable lives (due to skilled physicians and a strong will to live) and a few will enjoy remission.

Their stories were so emotional I often couldn't sleep at night, wishing I could help them; hoping for better days ahead with better drugs available, better health plans and more caring doctors.

Yet all have come to terms with their illness, and often talked about keeping true to their faith, helping others less fortunate than them and making every day count.

One of the most optimistic was Tim Fairholm, who died of a lupus-related aneurysm before this book was published. I had the honor of working with him and becoming his friend, as well as sharing the same rheumatologist at UCLA. It was in the waiting room that we bonded and made light of our ailments. Our rheumatologist, Dr. Jennifer Grossman, told us her staff often talked about how we cheered up the entire waiting room with laughter instead of tears, and I owe that to Tim. He showed me—and many others—how to live with humor and dignity and not cower in the face of this unkind disease.

Talk about lessons in humanity.

You have to accept
and the only
is that
with the best

whatever comes,
important thing
you meet it
you have to give.

—ELEANOR ROOSEVELT